CAKESMITHS

THE COFFEE SHOP CAKE SPECIALISTS

MOSSGIEL

ESTD 1841

THOMSON'S

COFFEE ROASTERS

Victoria Arduino

1905

FOR BREW FREAKS, BEAN GEEKS AND THE SIMPLY CURIOUS ...

Published by Salt Media Ltd 2019

A catalogue record of the book is available from the British Library.

www.saltmedia.co.uk
Tel: 01271 859299
Email: ideas@saltmedia.co.uk

Salt Media *Independent Coffee Guide* team: Richard Bailey, Nick Cooper, Sophie Ellis, Clare Hunt, Kathryn Lewis, Tamsin Powell, Jo Rees, Rosanna Rothery, Amy Sargeant, Christopher Sheppard, Dale Stiling, Mark Tibbles and Selena Young.
Design and illustration: Salt Media

A big thank you to the *Independent Coffee Guide* committee (meet them on page 150) for their expertise and enthusiasm, **our headline sponsors** iZettle and KeepCup, **and sponsors** Almond Breeze, Cakesmiths, Henny & Joe's, Mossgiel Farm, Olam Specialty Coffee, Thomson's Coffee Roasters and Victoria Arduino.

Coffee shops, cafes and roasters are invited to be included in the guide based on meeting criteria set by the committee, which includes the use of speciality beans, providing a high quality coffee experience for visitors and being independently run.

For information on the Ireland, The North and North Wales, and South West and South Wales *Independent Coffee Guides*, visit:

www.indycoffee.guide
@indycoffeeguide
@indycoffeeguide

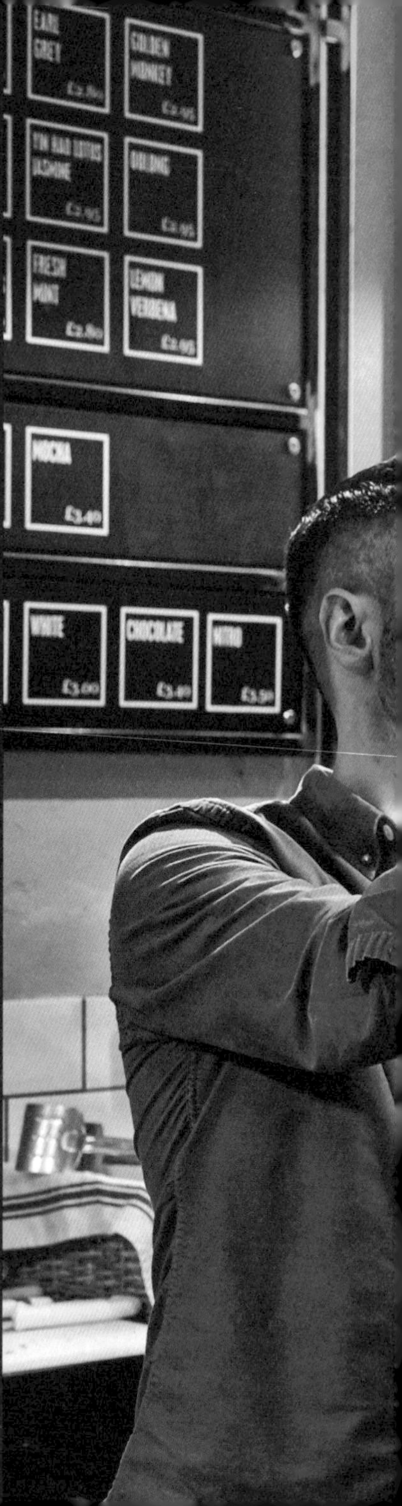

№63
BREW LAB

CONTENTS

PAGE

Photo: Natasha Kapur

WELCOME

It's been a year of new arrivals, exciting expansions and amplified eco awareness for Scotland's booming speciality scene – an inspiring evolution to be part of (and cheer on from the sidelines).

In this fourth edition, you'll find lots of fresh faces appearing alongside the country's established coffee shops and roasteries. From Fort William to Dumfries, new venues map the continued outwards spread of quality coffee from the speciality hubs of Edinburgh and Glasgow – as well as the growth of cafe culture within them.

Sustainability is high on the agenda and, since David Attenborough shone the spotlight on the uncomfortable truth about plastics, increasing numbers of consumers have ditched single-use. We find out how some of Scotland's eco champs are changing the game on page 22.

Coffee's fifth wave has also seen the arrival of a host of sister outposts this year: boutique chains offering further resistance to the multinational coffee shops.

Whether you're after new experiences or revel in familiarity, you'll find this year's guide bang up-to-date and crammed with lip-smackingly good finds.

What a time to be exploring coffee ...

Kathryn Lewis

Editor

Indy Coffee Guides

@indycoffeeguide

@indycoffeeguide

£25.00
ENTER PIN
Coffee
Croissant
Total
£8.50

A COFFEE WITH LILLA VALTER

THE SCOTTISH AEROPRESS CHAMPION AND HABITAT CAFE BARISTA TALKS FIRST TIMES AND PET PEEVES

Thanks to my grandfather, I was pretty much addicted to coffee by the age of 12. I was probably around six when I had my first ever cup, which was overly sweetened with sugar to disguise the taste. It wasn't necessarily the coffee that I enjoyed but the social experience and the opportunity to sit down and spend time with my grandfather.

My first introduction to speciality coffee was at university in Budapest. My campus was next door to Tamp & Pull, one of the city's first speciality shops, where I ended up spending a lot of time. The baristas were chatty, informative and we quickly became friends. When I graduated, I decided to give the barista life a go for a bit – and got hooked.

Due to rising rents I decided to leave Budapest in the summer of 2017 and set off for Scotland. A couple of friends who'd roasted at Steampunk in North Berwick told me about a speciality coffee shop in Aberfeldy, which wasn't so far away from where I was living in Pitlochry. I got in touch with owner Mike Haggerton and started working at Habitat at the start of 2018.

Competing in the World AeroPress Championship was amazing but my most memorable experience was a visit to Ona Coffee when I was in Sydney. I'd always wanted to go and it didn't disappoint. I tried a fantastic Colombian geisha and the Ethiopian beans which they had roasted for WBC 2018 winner Agnieszka Rojewska. It wasn't just the taste of the coffee which made it an incredible experience but the care and passion that the baristas put into their craft – they were effortlessly professional and easy-going at the same time.

My all-time favourite is a Kieni Kenyan coffee from The Coffee Collective. I've got a subscription with the Copenhagen roasters so drink a lot of their beans. At Habitat we often use Has Bean and I really love their El Salvador Finca Las Brumas Wild Forest Project coffee, served as filter.

I get frustrated when customers order soya milk. There are so many good alternatives which don't separate when combined with coffee and can actually stand up to latte art. If someone orders soya, I usually suggest oat milk instead.

My brunch order used to be avocado, but since I moved to Scotland I've become a big fan of the fry up. I'm talking eggs, haggis, black pudding – the full works. If I'm cooking brunch at home in the wee hamlet of Dull, I'll make something like smoked salmon and scrambled eggs or get creative – my boyfriend and I started the Dull Breakfast Club (@DullBreakfastClub) on Instagram.

Living in the Highlands makes it harder to predict where the speciality coffee scene will go next. It's clear that the interest in speciality is continuing to grow in the cities but there are still stumbling blocks when you're in a rural location. Habitat has proved that a speciality set-up can work outside of Edinburgh or Glasgow, but there are issues when it comes to staffing and seasonality.

IN SEARCH OF THE GREAT BARISTA

Industry experience, speciality knowledge and technical ability are the essential holy trinity, but what separates a good barista from a truly great one? We asked the pros ...

TODD JOHNSON & ZACH WILLIAMS

WILLIAMS & JOHNSON COFFEE CO.

'A lot of the qualities of a good barista come down to customer service. Welcoming people when they enter the cafe and getting to know regulars are really important. Customers who visit on a regular basis often return for the human interaction, so asking how their day is going makes a lasting impression.

'Being able to work in a team is another desirable skill and vital for consistency. Regulars become regulars because they know that the coffee is going to taste great – regardless of who made it. The barista who opens the cafe will dial in the espresso and they need to relay that information to the team so that every cup that day is as good as the first.'

HOLLIE PETRIE

SPIDER ON A BICYCLE

'While a solid knowledge of coffee and a technical skill set is great, the ability to multitask is important for a good barista. You can teach people how to brew coffee but teaching multitasking and customer service skills is much harder. This is amplified within indie coffee shops as a smaller set-up means that the barista will have to adopt different roles throughout the day – one minute they could be pouring a flat white, the next washing dishes, serving at the till or even baking.'

'ENTHUSIASM, CREATIVITY, CURIOSITY AND AN UNYIELDING COMMITMENT TO QUALITY'

MARK DONALD

THE MILKMAN

'A barista needs to have the knowledge to get the most out of the coffee they're serving. They also need to have the social skills to interact with the customer without coming across as pretentious.

'A lot of people won't set foot in speciality shops because they feel intimidated but we want to open up quality coffee to a spectrum of people with different backgrounds. Having a positive attitude and friendly demeanour helps people feel at ease.

'Being organised, tidy and proactive are also key attributes which contribute to efficient workflow. Being good at these will have a direct impact on the team you're working with and the smooth running of the cafe.'

'THERE'S NO ROOM FOR SHOW PONIES'

LISA CATHRO

ZEST CAFE

'A good barista is someone who cares about what they're doing and the customers they're serving. There's no room for show ponies. A willingness to learn is important too and people learn the most when they're teaching or helping someone else to improve their skills.'

ADELE MCPHEE

WILLOW GROVE

'Being a great barista isn't as simple as training on an espresso machine – it takes years of practice with lots of contributing factors along the way.

'Finding a good mentor is key – someone who is both a coffee specialist and an enthusiast. Be it a skilled barista who can teach the subtleties of the role or a roaster who can introduce the process and the diversity of beans, with a great teacher it becomes clear there's more to speciality coffee than just pulling a shot.'

GERARD BROWNE

SHAMROCK AND THISTLE

'Enthusiasm, creativity, curiosity and an unyielding commitment to quality are the four pillars from which every barista should work.

'Paying respect to the supply chain and having gratitude for the significant amount of labour that has gone into getting each bean from plant to cup is key. Baristas should honour this process in the careful and skilled preparation of the coffee.

'And serving the coffee with a smile and beautiful latte art keeps the customers coming back.'

'THERE'S MORE TO SPECIALITY COFFEE THAN JUST PULLING A SHOT'

ECO GAME-CHANGERS

From weigh-your-own lunches and zero-waste shopping to refashioned coffee grounds and slurping beer from a KeepCup, the speciality community is getting creative in its ethical efforts. Meet the game-changers spearheading sustainability in Scotland

Photo: @ameliaclaudia

THE WILDCAT, FORT WILLIAM

A speciality-shaped hole and lack of vegan options planted the seed for Fort William's first eco-conscious cafe

'IF WE DON'T TACKLE CLIMATE CHANGE, THERE WON'T BE ANY COFFEE PLANTS'

'We hadn't planned to open a speciality coffee shop,' admits Wildcat co-owner Stephen Kershaw. *'My partner Deanna and I had worked at an environmentally-conscious cafe in London which was where we began to explore speciality. When we moved to the Highlands, we noticed a lack of both good coffee and vegan options and wondered if we could spread the word about conscientious consumption while indulging our passions for both.*

'Our initial plan was to start a cafe which created a great impression of vegan food and only used ethical and organic ingredients (where possible) as they have the lowest environmental impact. It was also important to us that every decision would take into consideration the staff, suppliers and customers in order to leave the community a better place.

'We think we've done a good job at keeping to these ideals. The Wildcat Cafe has a complete ban on single-use cups, only uses plant-based milks, 95 per cent of the menu is organic and there's a zero-waste shopping area with plastic-free food hoppers. We've been amazed at how quickly we've been adopted into the community and the feedback from locals and tourists has been fantastic.

'It hasn't all been plain sailing, of course. Some people simply won't give us a try because we don't use "proper milk" or serve cheese toasties. Bringing a reusable cup still hasn't become second nature either, and some customers have grown frustrated with the inconvenience, even though we'll lend anyone a mug if they promise to bring it back. That said, overcoming these bumps is incredibly rewarding and we're proud to be leading the way here.

'If we don't tackle climate change, there won't be any coffee plants. Small businesses can adapt and change the way they do things much faster than the chains.'

GREEN®
GREEN®

GLASGOW COFFEE FESTIVAL

Teaming up with sustainably savvy KeepCup, Glasgow Coffee Festival became the UK's first disposable-free coffee fest in 2018 – and saved 18,000 single-use cups from heading to landfill

'WE SAVED OVER 18,000 DISPOSABLE CUPS FROM GOING TO LANDFILL'

'We'd wanted to find a way around the disposable cup conundrum since we launched the festival four years ago but the logistics always seemed like an insurmountable challenge,' says Glasgow Coffee Festival and Dear Green Coffee Roasters founder Lisa Lawson. *'I was over the moon when KeepCup partnered with us to make the idea of a reusable only set-up a reality.'*

'The first task was to encourage festival-goers to bring their own reusable,' explains KeepCup's Jack Ravenscroft, *'anything from a treasured cork KeepCup to an upcycled jam jar.*

'Anyone who couldn't bring their own could rent a KeepCup for the duration of the event and get their money back on the way out. Eight wash stations around the venue allowed festival-goers to try as many coffees as they liked, while an amazing group of GCF volunteers made sure everything ran smoothly.

'Over two days we saved over 18,000 disposable cups from going to landfill, though La Marzocco also used the loan-scheme for beers at the after-party so the true number was even higher. The festival also worked with Mossgiel Farm to supply milk for the show in glass bottles which saved 412 plastic containers going in the bin.'

'The response from the attendees and exhibitors was overwhelming,' adds Lisa. *'It proves that consumers are ready to make the switch to reusable cups – and that indie coffee businesses are willing to support them.'*

LUNCH

FOODSTORY ZERO, ABERDEEN

Students arrive armed with reusable cups, takeaway containers and eco-friendly cutlery at Foodstory's new zero-waste cafe at the University of Aberdeen

'THE COFFEE OPERATION ALONE WAS ALARMINGLY WASTEFUL'

'*Opening a second cafe is like having a second child,*' explains Foodstory co-founder Sandy McKinnon, who launched the speciality cafe in Aberdeen in 2013 with Lara Bishop. '*When you have the first one you learn as you go but when the second comes along you've got a grounding in the basics, know what to expect and can predict the bumps in the road ahead.*

'*Sustainability and an awareness of the environment have always been key values at Foodstory but, when we launched the original venue, we came across hurdles we hadn't foreseen. When we had the chance to open a cafe space within the University of Aberdeen we took the blank canvas – and our experience – as an opportunity to challenge the status quo.*

'*We were astonished at the amount of waste a business could produce. The coffee operation alone – non-recyclable bean packaging, disposable cups and piles of plastic milk bottles – was alarmingly wasteful. The new cafe (which, with ten seats, is mostly a takeaway set-up) is zero-waste. We encourage customers to bring refillable cups for drinks, takeaway containers for food and reusable cutlery. Milk is delivered in glass bottles by a local dairy which are then collected again; coffee beans arrive in custom-made reusable tubs from Obadiah Collective in Edinburgh; food is served in repurposed Tupperware containers and cleaning materials such as blue cloths are biodegradable.*

'*The reaction has been mostly positive and the majority of our customers are behind the concept which is really rewarding as we're essentially challenging the community to change their daily habits.*

'*At the moment we're the only ones doing this around here. In five years I hope the zero-waste set-up will be the norm.*'

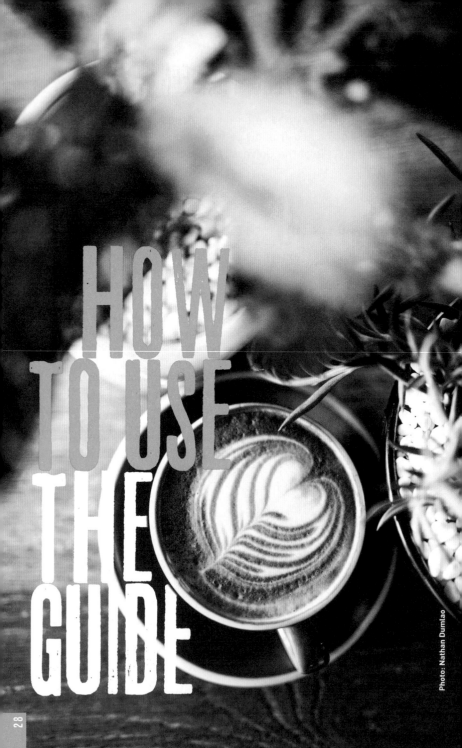

HOW TO USE THE GUIDE

Photo: Nathan Dumlao

CAFES

Coffee shops and cafes where you can drink top-notch speciality coffee. We've split the guide into areas to help you find places near you.

ROASTERS

Meet the leading speciality coffee roasters in Scotland and discover where to source beans. Find them after the cafes in each area.

MAPS

Every cafe and roastery has a number so you can find them either on the area map at the start of each section, or on the detailed city maps.

MORE GOOD STUFF

Discover **MORE GOOD CUPS** and **MORE GOOD ROASTERS** at the back of the book.

Don't forget to let us know how you get on as you explore the best speciality cafes and roasteries.

WWW.INDYCOFFEE.GUIDE

@indycoffeeguide @indycoffeeguide

YOUR
ADVENTURES
START
HERE
№62
HULA JUICE BAR

MAPS

WE'VE SPLIT SCOTLAND INTO AREAS TO MAKE IT EASIER TO FIND VENUES AND ROASTERS

1
3
4
2

AREA 1

№17
SPIDER ON A BICYCLE

CAFE

1 The Ceilidh Place
2 Cafe Margot
3 Cafe Margot... to go
4 Caora Dhubh Coffee Company
5 Cafe Sia
6 The Wildcat
7 Slaughterhouse Coffee
8 Little Bird Coffee House
9 Speyside Coffee Roasting Co.
10 The Coffee Apothecary – Ellon
11 The Coffee Apothecary – Udny
12 Foodstory Zero
13 The Cult of Coffee
14 Foodstory
15 Figment
16 Shamrock and Thistle
17 Spider on a Bicycle

ROASTER

18 Figment Coffee Company

Find more good cafes and roasters on pages 144-148

*All locations are approximate

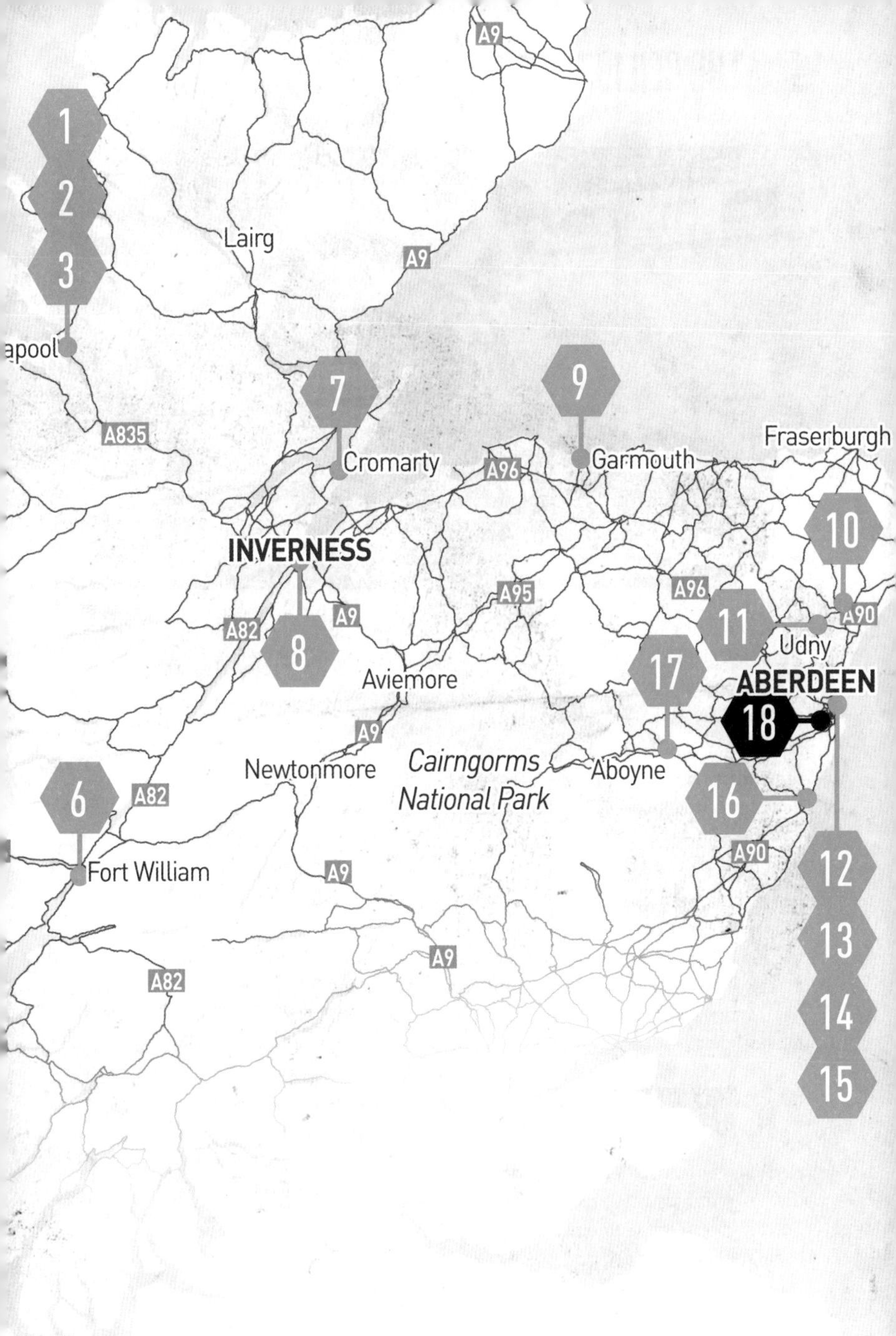
A9
1
2
3
Lairg
A9
apool
7
9
A835
Cromarty
A96
Garmouth
Fraserburgh
INVERNESS
10
A95
A96
A9
A82
11
A90
8
Udny
17
Aviemore
ABERDEEN
18
A9
Newtonmore
Cairngorms
National Park
Aboyne
6
A82
16
A90
Fort William
12
A9
13
A9
A82
14
15

MAP № 1 THE CEILIDH PLACE

12-14 West Argyle Street, Ullapool, Ross-shire, IV26 2TY

As one of the most northerly spots in the UK serving quality coffee, The Ceilidh Place is a beacon of speciality for visitors exploring the beautiful region of Wester Ross.

Making a detour to this family-run retreat is well worth the effort and walkers, adventurers and tourists all beat a path to its door. The Ullapool lodge also houses a restaurant, bookshop, gallery and events space alongside the cosy coffee shop.

Kick off an overnight stop with a sweet and fruity Glen Lyon Red Stag cappuccino and raisin-studded scone while perusing a classic from The Ceilidh's eclectic collection of books. After dinner, head to the bar – there's often live music – to explore the shelf of Islands' gins.

INSIDER'S TIP **CHECK OUT THE BUSY CALENDAR OF EVENTS SO YOU CAN PLAN YOUR TRIP TO COINCIDE**

Perthshire-roasted beans make another appearance the next morning when they're served alongside hearty Scottish breakfasts – the perfect fuel for a day of Highlands adventures.

ESTABLISHED
1970

KEY ROASTER
Glen Lyon Coffee Roasters

BREWING METHOD
Espresso, cafetiere

MACHINE
Conti

GRINDER
Mahlkonig K30

OPENING HOURS
Mon-Sun 8am-11pm

Gluten FREE

WIFI

CYCLE FRIENDLY

OUTDOOR seating

www.theceilidhplace.com T: 01854 612103

@theceilidhplace @theceilidhplace @1970ceil

MAP № 2 CAFE MARGOT

West Argyle Street, Ullapool, Ross-shire, IV26 2TY

Appetites sharpened by Loch Broom's salty breeze call for a first-rate brew – and happily, Cafe Margot is on hand to deliver the goods.

The cafe's location (above an outdoorsy shop) is unassuming, but visitors are rewarded for pushing through the cagoules with speciality coffee and a temptingly eclectic menu.

A spanking new refurb means everything's bright and, as the seating area shares space with a photographic gallery, there's plenty to entertain the eye, too.

Glasgow's Dear Green supply the stalwart beans, while guest roasters are invited to celebrate seasonality and flavour diversity. An impressive Strada AV handles espresso duties, with grinding managed by the trio of Mazzer Kolds and an EK43.

FRESHEN YOUR PALATE AFTER AN ESPRESSO WITH A SCOOP OF AWARD WINNING HOMEMADE GELATO

The Margot crew are especially proud of their artisan breads, all of which are knocked up on-site. They make perfect bedfellows for imaginative made-to-order salads and cooked brekkies. Veggies and vegans won't find themselves struggling for a hearty lunch either, with dishes such as beetroot and chickpea burgers on offer.

ESTABLISHED
2019

KEY ROASTER
Dear Green Coffee Roasters

BREWING METHOD
Espresso, filter

MACHINE
La Marzocco Strada AV ABR

GRINDER
Mazzer Kold x 3, Mahlkonig EK43

OPENING HOURS

Mon-Sun 8am-5pm

www.cafemargot.co.uk T: 07955 122029

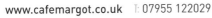

@cafe_margot @margot_cafe

MAP № 3 CAFE MARGOT... TO GO

4 West Argyle Street, Ullapool, Ross-shire, IV23 2RZ

Coffee and ice cream: it's a killer combo by anyone's reckoning. But make that small-batch roasted specialily coffee and award winning artisan gelato and you've got a whole other ball game going on.

Set just a lick from the shores of Loch Broom, Cafe Margot's take-out-only outpost ensures sweet caffeinated thrills for Ullapool's visiting coffee fiends. Expect carefully roasted beans as espresso or batch brew from the speciality leg of London's Drury roastery, as well as toothsome guests from Dear Green in Glasgow and Bath's Colonna Coffee.

While trade flocks in for the ices and brews, Margot also has another string to its bow in the shape of homemade artisan bread. As you dash to catch your ferry from the nearby terminal, grab a little something for your packed lunch.

PERCH BY THE LOCH AND WATCH THE BOBBING BOATS AS YOU SAVOUR AN ESPRESSO

In addition to carby faves such as stuffed focaccia sandwiches, fresh salads inspired by Middle Eastern flavours feature. And everything's handmade (using organic ingredients where possible) at Margot's sister cafe across the road.

ESTABLISHED
2017

KEY ROASTER
Drury Tea & Coffee

BREWING METHOD
Espresso, batch brew, cold brew, filter

MACHINE
Rancilio Classe 9

GRINDER
Ceado E37 x 3, Ceado E8D

OPENING HOURS
Apr-Oct **8**am-**5**pm

Gluten FREE

www.cafemargot.co.uk T: 01854 612228

f @gelatoullapool @gelato_ullapool @gelato_ullapool

MAP № 4 CAORA DHUBH COFFEE COMPANY

Carbost, Isle of Skye, IV47 8SR

If you need proof that nowhere's too remote for speciality coffee, make tracks to this cosy shack teetering on the shore of Skye's Loch Harport.

From the outside, Caora Dhubh, with its distinctive black sheep logo, looks as rugged as the surrounding craggy coast, however, a welcoming interior offers respite from blustery weather and is infused with heady aromas wafting from the La Marzocco.

INSIDER'S TIP **SUGAR JUNKIE? TRY EDINBURGH'S COCO CHOCOLATIER MELTED INTO A RICH HOT CHOCOLATE**

It's still early days for Jamie Fletcher and the Caora Dhubh crew, but they're building on their initial success and have their sights set on expanding the offering during 2019. Beans make the trip from Edinburgh's Artisan Roast and are expertly crafted into espresso-based brews, while a spanking new EK43 grinder promises to pave the way for more seasonal single origins.

A commitment to Scottish producers is reflected in locally made bakes. Keep your fingers crossed that there's a slice of cousin Cathy's carrot cake left to keep your cappuccino company when you make the trip. There's a new menu of savouries to reward intrepid visitors, too.

ESTABLISHED
2017

KEY ROASTER
Artisan Roast Coffee Roasters

BREWING METHOD
Espresso, filter

MACHINE
La Marzocco FB70

GRINDER
Mythos One, Mahlkonig EK43

OPENING HOURS
Mar-Nov **10**am-**5**pm

www.caoradhubh.com T: 01478 640666

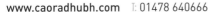

@caoradhubhcoffee @caoradhubh

MAP № 5 CAFE SIA

Ford Road, Broadford, Isle of Skye, IV49 9AB

A coffee shop on the Isle of Skye isn't the first place you'd expect to find authentic Italian pizza. Yet you'll discover a little slice of Italy at Cafe Sia, thanks to owner Tom Eveling and team.

After co-managing a Michelin starred hotel on the island for several years, Tom packed in the country lodge life and drove all the way to Pisa to pick up a wood-fired oven so he could share his passion for great pizza, coffee and wine with Skye's hungry visitors (and locals).

INSIDER'S TIP FINISH A DAY ON THE ISLAND WITH AN ESPRESSO AND WEE DRAM ON THE TERRACE

The cafe's unique blend of Scot/Med inspo influences everything: from pizza toppings (try the Sia Formaggi oozing with six Scottish and Italian cheeses) to coffee (the affogato is crafted from beans roasted at Skye Coffee Roasters and homemade gelato).

If you're looking for a straight caffeine shot, home roasted beans are served as espresso and filter, with guest options from Aberfeldy's Glen Lyon available on a second grinder. After dark, 'spros are swapped for glasses of biodynamic and organic wine, as well as craft beers from a local micro brewery.

ESTABLISHED
2014

KEY ROASTER
Skye Coffee Roasters

BREWING METHOD
Espresso

MACHINE
Fracino Contempo

GRINDER
Mahlkonig

OPENING HOURS
Mon-Fri 10am-9pm
(seasonal opening hours)

Gluten FREE

BEANS AVAILABLE INSTORE

www.cafesia.co.uk T: 01471 822616

MAP № 6 THE WILDCAT

21 High Street, Fort William, Highlands, PH33 6DH

Photos: Amelia Claudia

The indie coffee scene may have been at the forefront of hospitality's eco revolution for many years, but Fort William's first speciality coffee shop is taking the war on waste a step further.

Forget biodegradable cups, at The Wildcat take-out drinks are a strictly reusable set-up (with porcelain mugs if you're caught KeepCup short). And coffee is served exclusively with plant-based milk – choose from a selection of organic varieties.

INSIDER'S TIP BRING REUSABLE CONTAINERS TO STOCK UP ON GRAINS AND BEANS FROM THE WEIGH-YOUR-OWN DISPENSERS

It's not just caffeine kicks which are easy on the conscience either: the colourful lunch plates are made in-house from raw (mainly organic) vegan ingredients, there's a zero-waste wholefood retail section and a cosy corner with a stack of environmental books and mags.

Beans from Scottish roasters Dear Green and Steampunk fuel lazy afternoons (best with a chunk of homemade cake), and there are guest appearances from Glasgow's The Good Coffee Cartel in summer when batch brew and AeroPress are in high demand.

ESTABLISHED
2018

KEY ROASTER
Dear Green Coffee Roasters

BREWING METHOD
Espresso, V60, batch brew, AeroPress, cold brew

MACHINE
La Marzocco Strada AV

GRINDER
Victoria Arduino Mythos One, Mahlkonig EK43

OPENING HOURS
Mon-Sat 8am-5.30pm
Sun 9am-4.30pm

www.wildcatcafe.co.uk T: 01397 698856

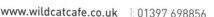

f @thewildcatfortwilliam @thewildcatcafe @thewildcatfortwilliam

MAP № 7 SLAUGHTERHOUSE COFFEE

Marine Terrace North, Cromarty to Nigg ferry slipway, Cromarty, Highlands, IV11 8XZ

If you're traversing the Black Isle and fancy a little speciality coffee sipping while dolphin, bird and boat spotting, don't miss the opportunity to check out this characterful cabin on the tip of Cromarty.

A mere pebble's skim from where the Cromarty-Nigg ferry chugs back and forth during the summer months, Slaughterhouse Coffee is in a unique spot for amazing views while enjoying an espresso or pourover of note.

Its Aussie owner, Tony Vandyke, serves his own roasted Vandyke Brothers blend (a Brazilian, Indian and Ethiopian mix) as well as beans from west Yorkshire guest, Dark Woods.

INSIDER'S TIP **BROWSE THE IMPRESSIVE ARRAY OF BEANS TO BUY FOR HOME BREWING**

The rustic shed, which has packing-crate seating and cable-reel tables for alfresco sipping, also serves sourdough and fruit bread toast from the award winning Wild Hearth Bakery, plus a modest selection of homemade snacks.

There are many good reasons to visit this historic Highlands town, but a welcoming vibe and the chance to drink in views across Cromarty Firth with a great coffee in hand is definitely high on the list.

ESTABLISHED
2017

KEY ROASTER
Vandyke Brothers Specialty Coffee

BREWING METHOD
Espresso, filter, cold brew

MACHINE
La Marzocco Linea PB

GRINDER
Mazzer Kold, Mahlkonig EK43

OPENING HOURS
Mon-Sun 8am-2pm

T: 07494 492695

@vandykebros @vandykebros

MAP № 8 LITTLE BIRD COFFEE HOUSE

Ironworks Venue, 122b Academy Street, Inverness, IV1 1LX

Proving that pop-ups can turn into successful permanent ventures, Little Bird Coffee House has expertly eased Inverness' speciality cravings since it launched as a short term project in 2015.

In a corner of Academy Street music venue, Ironworks, Jay, Julie and George have managed to squeeze a well-stocked brew bar, espresso machine and short 'n' sweet food offering into a staggeringly small space.

Even more impressive is the number of roasters which have taken their turn in the grinder this year (between house beans from Bailies and The Good Coffee Cartel). Cardiff's Hard Lines, Dublin's Cloud Picker and Galway's Calendar Coffee were just three of 2018's nine-strong line-up.

INSIDER'S TIP THE BISCOFF ROCKY ROAD IS KNOWN TO THE LOCALS AS "CRACK"

A hub for all things speciality in the town, Little Bird also hosts regular cuppings and caffeinated events for visitors and local brew buffs. Pick up bags of beans, the latest issue of *Caffeine* magazine and soap made from recycled coffee grounds, too.

ESTABLISHED
2015

KEY ROASTER
Multiple roasters

BREWING METHOD
Espresso, V60, AeroPress

MACHINE
La Marzocco PB

GRINDER
Mahlkonig K30 Air

OPENING HOURS
Mon-Fri
8.30am-2.30pm
Sat 10am-2pm

T: 07740 124659

f @littlebirdcoffeehouse · @lbcoffeehouse · @littlebirdcoffee

MAP № 9 SPEYSIDE COFFEE ROASTING CO.

The Garmouth Hotel, South Road, Garmouth, Moray, IV32 7LU

There are plenty of worthy reasons to make a detour to this village meeting place which is a fascinating hybrid of roastery, cafe, pub, restaurant and hotel. However, the most compelling is its seriously smooth and lightly roasted Brazilian coffee – and the opportunity to witness the roasting alchemy first hand.

You can also sip a local ale or malt whisky at the bar, scoff delish homemade cakes (think raspberry and cream swiss roll), pamper your pooch with doggy scones, take advantage of unusual shopping opps (check out the soya candles) and, in winter, relax next to a roaring fire.

INSIDER'S TIP **BUY A BEE BOMB AND DO A SPOT OF ECO-FRIENDLY GUERRILLA GARDENING**

With owners Jody and Grant Spence at the helm, innovative ideas pop up all the time. Collaborations include a coffee porter with Windswept brewery, a Moray Mocha gin with local distillers El:Gin and a coffee candle crafted in coordination with Mulderie Wood.

And if it's the house coffee and tasty brunches and lunches (from vegan wellington to battered haddock) that lure people in, it's the art exhibitions, wine and cheese events, and cocktail nights that turn them into loyal fans.

ESTABLISHED
2017

KEY ROASTER
Speyside Coffee Roasting Co.

BREWING METHOD
Espresso, filter, cafetiere

MACHINE
La San Marco

GRINDER
Mazzer, La San Marco

OPENING HOURS
Tue-Sun 11am-4pm

Gluten FREE

BEANS AVAILABLE INSTORE

www.speysidecoffee.co.uk T: 01343 870226

№14
FOODSTORY

MAP № 10 THE COFFEE APOTHECARY – ELLON

21 The Square, Ellon, Aberdeenshire, AB41 9JB

You know you're doing something right when the UK's biggest craft brewery asks you to open a coffee shop in its hometown.

For years the folk at BrewDog travelled the five miles from Ellon to Udny to get their speciality coffee fix so, when the brewery wanted to create somewhere its staff and guests could enjoy great food and incredible caffeine, they knew the team at The Coffee Apothecary would be perfect for the job.

INSIDER'S TIP FIVE CRAFT BEERS AND EXTENDED OPENING HOURS MAKE THIS A DAY-INTO-EVENING HANGOUT

The new outpost on The Square is twice the size of its sister cafe in Udny, though it's very much part of the Apothecary family. Aubergine-hued walls, drop lighting and the famous spend-a-penny bathroom flooring all refer to the original venue, as does the menu of locally sourced and homemade breakfast and lunch dishes.

Coffee also sticks with tradition here and co-owner – and chief barista – Jonny has replicated his La Marzocco/Mythos/EK43 set-up at the new space to showcase two espresso and two filter coffees from Edinburgh's Artisan Roast.

ESTABLISHED
2019

KEY ROASTER
Artisan Roast Coffee Roasters

BREWING METHOD
Espresso, Kalita Wave, cafetiere

MACHINE
La Marzocco Linea PB ABR, Marco SP9

GRINDER
Mythos One, Mahlkonig EK43

OPENING HOURS
Mon-Sun 8am-10pm

www.thecoffeeapothecary.co.uk T: 01358 721946

f @thecoffeeapothecaryellon @ellonapothecary @thecoffeeapothecaryellon

MAP № 11 THE COFFEE APOTHECARY – UDNY

Udny, Ellon, Aberdeenshire, AB41 7PQ

It's not often you find a speciality coffee house of this calibre which also delivers on the seasonal/homemade food front, but when you're located in rural Aberdeenshire, doing a lot of things well is kind of key.

Call into Udny's former post office on any given day and you're likely to find a healthy mix of locals and tourists road testing the latest single origin and tucking into hearty lunches (think locally-landed-hake tacos) and fat slices of the kitchen's latest sweet creation.

INSIDER'S TIP THE TEAM ARE HOT ON SPECIALITY KNOWLEDGE – PICK THEIR BRAINS ON BREWING TIPS

While the hyperlocal breakfast and lunch menus are a big draw, Apothecary's quality coffee offering provides the riches which tempt speciality-savvy travellers from their path. Choose from the two espressos and filters chalked up on the board, or test your palate with a tasting flight (the same coffee – brewed as espresso and filter) and explore the nuances to be found in different serve styles.

Fans can get a second helping of the Apothecary experience at its sister outlet in nearby Ellon, which opened in early 2019.

ESTABLISHED
2014

KEY ROASTER
Artisan Roast Coffee Roasters

BREWING METHOD
Espresso, Kalita Wave, cafetiere

MACHINE
La Marzocco Linea PB ABR, Marco SP9

GRINDER
Mythos One, Mahlkonig EK43

OPENING HOURS
Mon-Sun 9am-4pm

www.thecoffeeapothecary.co.uk T: 01651 842253

f @thecoffeeapothecary @udnyapothecary @thecoffeeapothecary

MAP № 12 FOODSTORY ZERO

Taylor Building, Regent Walk, University of Aberdeen, Aberdeen, AB24 3EB

A campus cafe with a distinct difference, Foodstory Zero takes the eco-conscious ethos of its city centre sister a step further. Outstanding coffee keeps scholarly brains ticking while the zero waste and packaging concept does everyone good.

Obadiah Collective supplies the cafe with beans roasted in Edinburgh with Aussie expertise. Coffee lovers have a straightforward choice between batch brew and espresso, so the quality of the roast has free rein to flaunt its flavour notes. And, in line with the environmental focus, Obadiah delivers the beans in vacuum-sealed containers which keep the coffee fresh without excess packaging.

INSIDER'S TIP THE SOURDOUGH TOASTIES AND TOASTED FLATBREADS ARE LUNCH BREAK GAME-CHANGERS

Foodstory Zero delivers where many others make vague promises: a reusable cup is a must if you want your brew to-go (though you can make use of donated vessels). And there's even a Belfast sink available so you can give your KeepCup a quick swill.

Eating well is as easy as drinking well and regulars can be found tucking into the wholesomely delish vegan and veggie offerings for which Foodstory has earned its rep.

ESTABLISHED
2018

KEY ROASTER
Obadiah Collective

BREWING METHOD
Espresso, batch brew

MACHINE
La Marzocco Linea

GRINDER
Mazzer Kold

OPENING HOURS
Mon-Fri
8.30am-4.30pm

www.foodstorycafe.co.uk

f @foodstoryzero @foodstoryzero

MAP № 13 THE CULT OF COFFEE

28 Esslemont Avenue, Aberdeen, AB25 1SN

A cult with coffee and cake at its heart? Sounds like one worth joining. This Aberdeen bolthole may have incorporated ancient and intriguing imagery into its logo (spy other symbols on the counter tiles) but don't fear secret rituals, as the only rite taking place here involves sipping coffee and nibbling amazing bakes.

The creed at Cult of Coffee centres around great beans prepared as espresso or Clever Dripper, with Artisan Roast's Janszoon inspiring devotion as the house blend. Other Scottish denominations – there are always two guests on the go for coffee devotees – include Machina, Unorthodox, Obadiah Collective and Holy Island.

INSIDER'S TIP CHECK OUT THE HANDMADE DOG BOWLS FOR FURRY VISITORS

Those wanting to opt out of the city's lunchtime frenzy head here for an oasis of calm where they can explore an ever-changing assortment of cakes and house-baked scones alongside great coffee, board games and a cool playlist. And, should you want to recreate it all at home, you can bag some beans and sign up for one of the in-house brewing courses, too.

ESTABLISHED
2017

KEY ROASTER
Artisan Roast Coffee Roasters

BREWING METHOD
Espresso, Clever Dripper

MACHINE
La Marzocco Linea PB

GRINDER
Mahlkonig EK43, Mazzer Major

OPENING HOURS
Mon-Sat 8.30am-5pm
Sun 9.30am-5pm
(extended in summer)

Gluten FREE

BEANS AVAILABLE INSTORE

T: 07793 406726

@thecultofcoffee @the_cult_of_coffee

MAP № 14 FOODSTORY

11-15 Thistle Street, Aberdeen, AB10 1XZ

It's been five years since a Kickstarter campaign brought the Foodstory concept to life. And the cafe continues to embody a thriving sense of inclusivity and integrity – the result of being lovingly hand-crafted by founders Sandy McKinnon, Lara Bishop and their community-focused crew.

Having blazed a vegan and veggie trail in the Granite City, Foodstory matches good food with equally impressive brews. Beans from Glasgow's Dear Green take the spotlight – look out for the bespoke Foodstory blend – while Obadiah Collective and Williams & Johnson take turns on the guest spot.

INSIDER'S TIP **KEEP AN EYE OPEN FOR THE LIVELY LINE-UP OF EVENTS HELD ABOVE THE CAFE**

A posse of grinders delivers the perfectly refined beans which are dripped through V60, squeezed via AeroPress or batch brewed in the Moccamaster. You'll also find beans (ready to brew at home) in the wholefood shop upstairs.

Food is plant-based and planet friendly, with everything (down to dressings) crafted in-house. Fresh salads and hearty hotpots make the most of local and organic produce.

ESTABLISHED
2013

KEY ROASTER
Dear Green Coffee Roasters

BREWING METHOD
Espresso, filter, batch brew, V60, AeroPress

MACHINE
La Marzocco Linea PB

GRINDER
Victoria Arduino Mythos One, Mahlkonig EK43, Mazzer Kold, Mazzer Robur

OPENING HOURS
Mon-Thu 8am-9pm
Fri 8am-10pm
Sat 9am-9pm
Sun 11am-3pm

Gluten FREE

BEANS AVAILABLE INSTORE

www.foodstorycafe.co.uk

@thefoodstorycafe @foodstorycoffee @foodstoryscotland

MAP № 15 FIGMENT

70 Countesswells Road, Aberdeen, AB15 7YJ

Locals couldn't believe their luck when they discovered that Aberdeen's newest addition wasn't only serving speciality-standard coffee but also dishing up delicious grub and cranking out craft beers 'til late.

Housed in a former supermarket in the city's West End, the huge all-day hangout is a bright, light-filled space in which to drink lip-smackingly good coffee, scoff something tasty on toast and gather the gang for post-work organic wines.

INSIDER'S TIP **SPOT THE 'SECRET' ART INSTALLATION BY LOCAL ARTIST KATIE GUTHRIE**

And, as if the Figment team didn't have enough on their plates, founder Neil Glover also decided to take roasting duties in-house, installing a nifty Diedrich.

'As an engineer, I wanted to blend science with the art of coffee making to deliver flavours unique to the terroir of each bean,' says Neil.

Start with a cup of the house blend, Wonderland, before taking a tour of single origin filters. And make sure you're packing a healthy appetite when you visit as the seasonal menus are developed with chef Jamie Scott of award winning The Newport Restaurant.

ESTABLISHED
2018

KEY ROASTER
Figment Coffee Company

BREWING METHOD
Espresso, Kalita Wave, Curtis batch brewer

MACHINE
Synesso

GRINDER
Mahlkonig Peak, Mahlkonig EK43

OPENING HOURS
Mon-Thu **7.30**am-**5**pm
Fri **7.30**am-**10**pm
Sat **8.30**am-**10**pm
Sun **8.30**am-**5**pm

www.figmentcoffee.com T: 01224 467500

@figmentcoffee @figmentcoffee @figmentcoffee

MAP № 16 SHAMROCK AND THISTLE

6 Arbuthnott Place, Stonehaven, Aberdeenshire, AB39 2JA

After a decade of blissfully-caffeinated living down under, Gerard and Sarah Browne felt compelled to bring their coffee passion with them when they returned home to Stonehaven.

The plan was to create a coffee house which was speciality-focused but not preachy – and the result is Shamrock and Thistle, which launched in 2017.

Duck into the vibrant coffee shop with its floor-to-ceiling life-of-the-coffee-bean mural and you'll find Gerard, Sarah and the friendly team fashioning micro lots (they switch up the roast monthly) via V60, Chemex and AeroPress, as well as crowd-pleasing Sacred Grounds espresso-based drinks.

TACKLE A STONEY STACKER FT. WAFFLES, BACON, HAGGIS, BLACK PUDDING, EGG, CHEESE AND BEANS

Shamrock's line-up of sweet and savoury temptations come in waffle and crêpe shapes and are aptly named after Scottish and Irish castles (a nod to the owners' Celtic heritages). The daily selection is chalked up above the counter and best followed by a lengthy walk around Stonehaven's pretty harbour.

ESTABLISHED
2017

KEY ROASTER
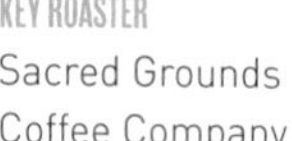
Sacred Grounds Coffee Company

BREWING METHOD
Espresso, V60, AeroPress, Chemex

MACHINE
La Marzocco Linea PB

GRINDER
Mazzer Robur E, Mahlkonig EK43

OPENING HOURS
Seasonal opening hours

Gluten FREE

T: 07764 715659

f @shamrockandthistlecoffee @shamrockandthistlecoffee

MAP № 17 SPIDER ON A BICYCLE

Unit 3, Station Square, Aboyne, Aberdeenshire, AB34 5HX

A couple of years ago it was nearly impossible to find great coffee in rural north-east Scotland, so many a road trip ended in caffeine-deprived disagreements and a lengthy detour to Aberdeen.

So when, in 2016, sisters Hollie and Emma Petrie launched a speciality coffee shop in Aboyne's former train station, both locals and passing coffee purists rejoiced at the new addition.

Two years on and Spider on a Bicycle (named after the sisters' favourite childhood book) has taken on a central role in the Highlands village. On Sundays you'll find the whole community gathering at Petrie senior's handmade tables to scoff the weekly brunch specials.

INSIDER'S TIP **GRAB A SPOT BY THE LOG BURNER AND TREAT YOURSELF TO A WEDGE OF VEGAN APPLE SLICE**

Comforting homemade fodder is matched by consistently great coffee, crafted on the trusty La Marzocco using beans from Papercup in Glasgow. Single origins from the roaster change with the seasons, though Hollie and Emma always choose something that's going to taste as delicious showered in steamed milk as it does straight-up as espresso.

ESTABLISHED
2016

KEY ROASTER
Papercup Coffee Roasters

BREWING METHOD
Espresso

MACHINE
La Marzocco Linea Classic

GRINDER
Nuova Simonelli

OPENING HOURS
Tue-Sat **8.30**am-**4.30**pm
Sun **9**am-**4.30**pm
(extended in summer)

www.spideronabicycle.com

f @spideronabicycle   @spideronabicycle

AREA 1 ROASTERS

MAP 18 FIGMENT COFFEE COMPANY

70 Countesswells Road, Aberdeen, AB15 7YJ

Mechanical engineer (and founder of Figment) Neil Glover and team know that their wholesale customers love coffee as much as they do and, together, they're pursuing the ultimate goal: a perfectly crafted cup.

With precision control over each roast on the trusty Diedrich, Neil and the gang offer just that via their variety of single origin roasts for espresso and filter.

'WE'RE ALL ABOUT QUALITY, CONSISTENCY AND FLAVOUR'

The seasonal Wonderland blend has its own fanbase and is particularly delicious with milk which develops the chocolate and caramel notes.

'*We're all about quality, consistency and flavour,*' says Neil. '*We combine the science and art of roasting to optimise every batch and bring out the flavours of the terroir.*'

Whether you're a cafe owner or a home brewer, deciding which of the beans to buy turns out to be the perfect excuse for an afternoon spent sipping and picking out leaves at Figment's spacious cafe next door.

ESTABLISHED
2018

ROASTER MAKE & SIZE
Diedrich IR-12
12kg

www.figmentcoffee.com T: 01224 467500

@figmentcoffee @figmentcoffee @figmentcoffee

AREA

LOCH LOMOND

CAFE

19 St Mocha Coffee Shop and Ice Cream Parlour
20 The Buffet Box
21 Kings Coffee & Books

ROASTER

37 Thomson's Coffee Roasters

Find more good cafes and roasters on pages 144-148

*All locations are approximate

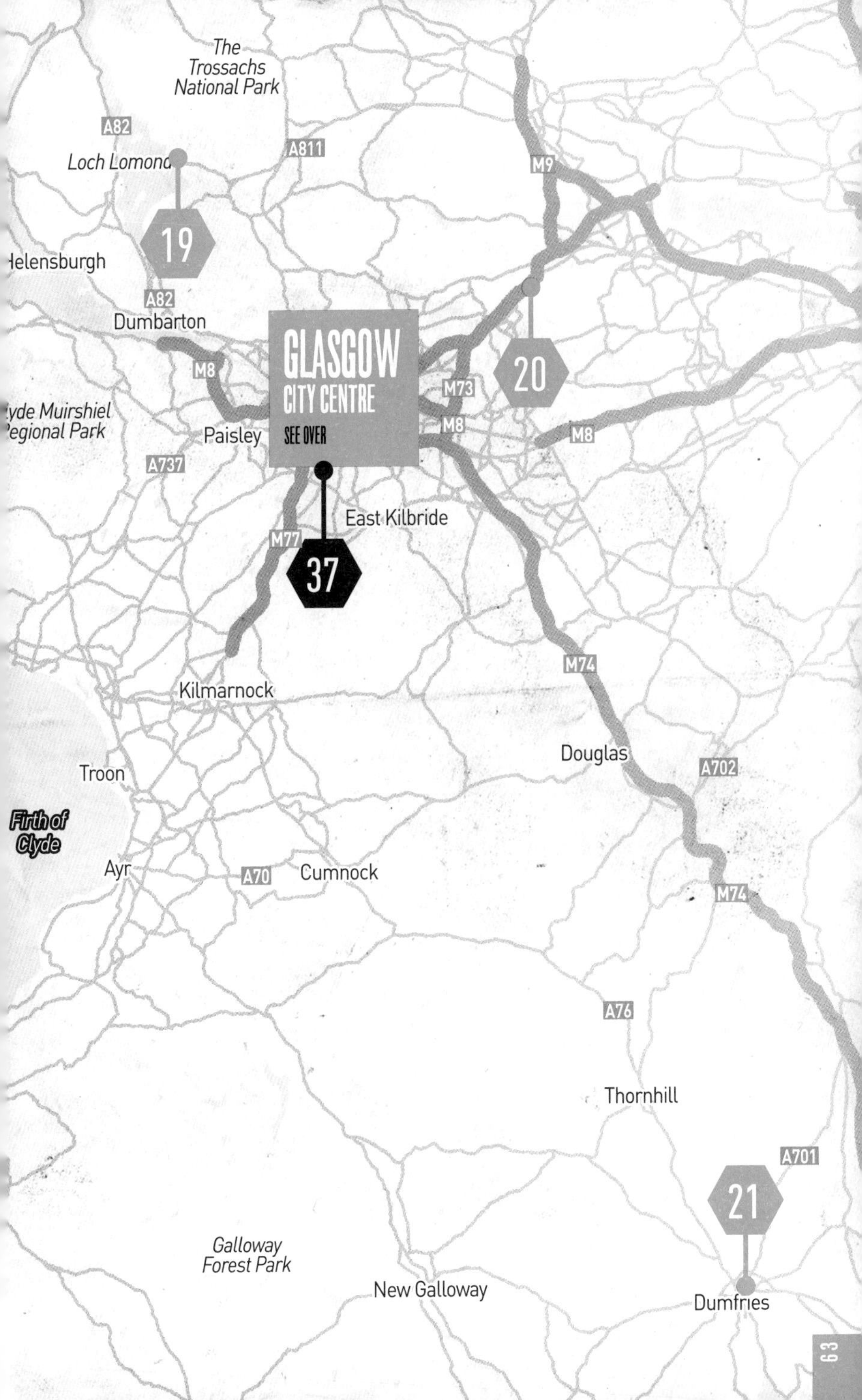
The Trossachs National Park
A82
Loch Lomond
A811
M9
19
Helensburgh
A82
Dumbarton
GLASGOW
CITY CENTRE
SEE OVER
M8
20
M73
M8
Paisley
M8
A737
East Kilbride
M77
37
M74
Kilmarnock
Douglas
A702
Troon
Firth of Clyde
Ayr
A70
Cumnock
M74
A76
Thornhill
A701
21
Galloway Forest Park
New Galloway
Dumfries

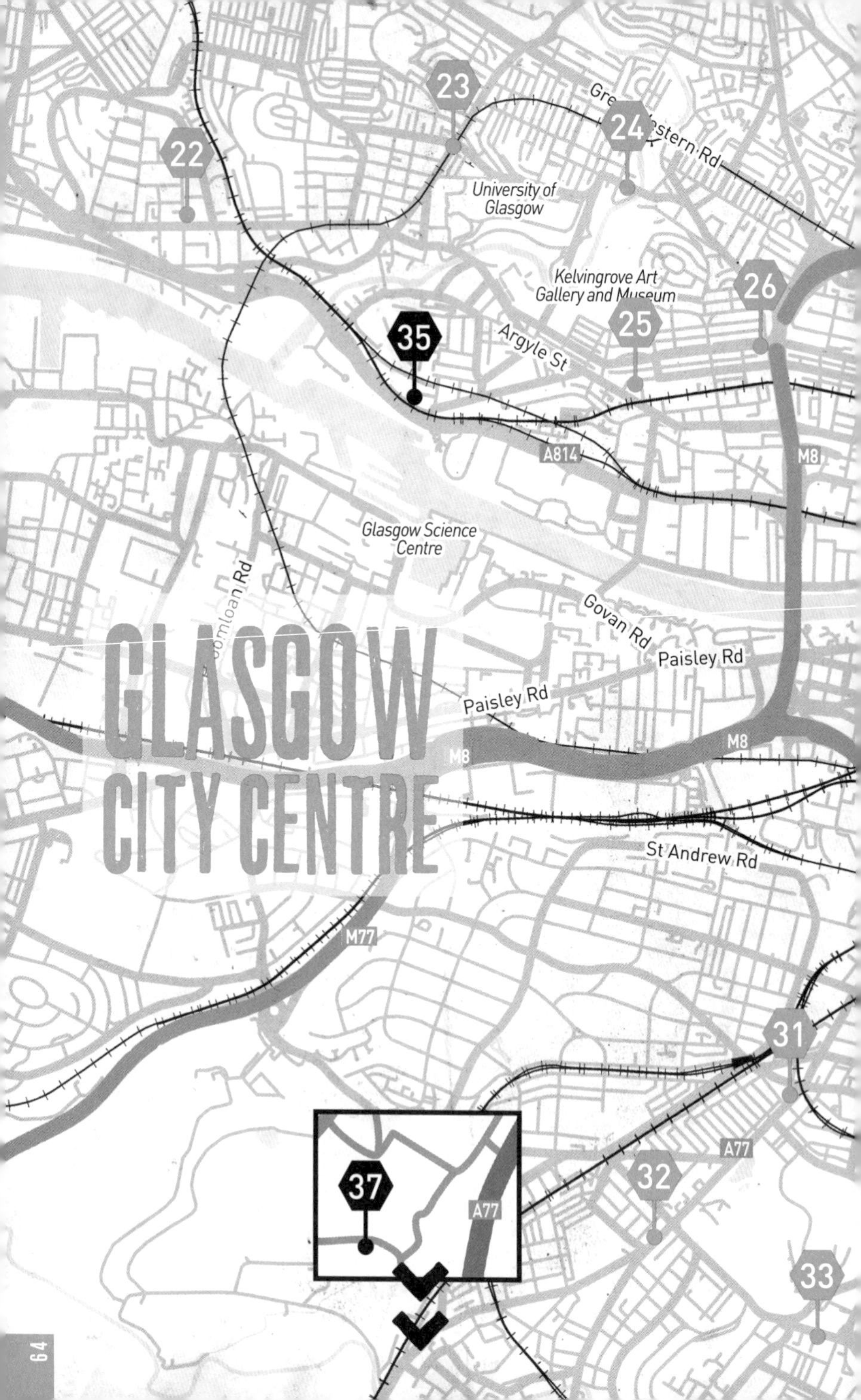
GLASGOW
CITY CENTRE
University of Glasgow
Kelvingrove Art Gallery and Museum
Argyle St
A814
M8
Glasgow Science Centre
Govan Rd
Paisley Rd
Paisley Rd
St Andrew Rd
M77
A77
A77
22
23
24
25
26
31
32
33
35
37

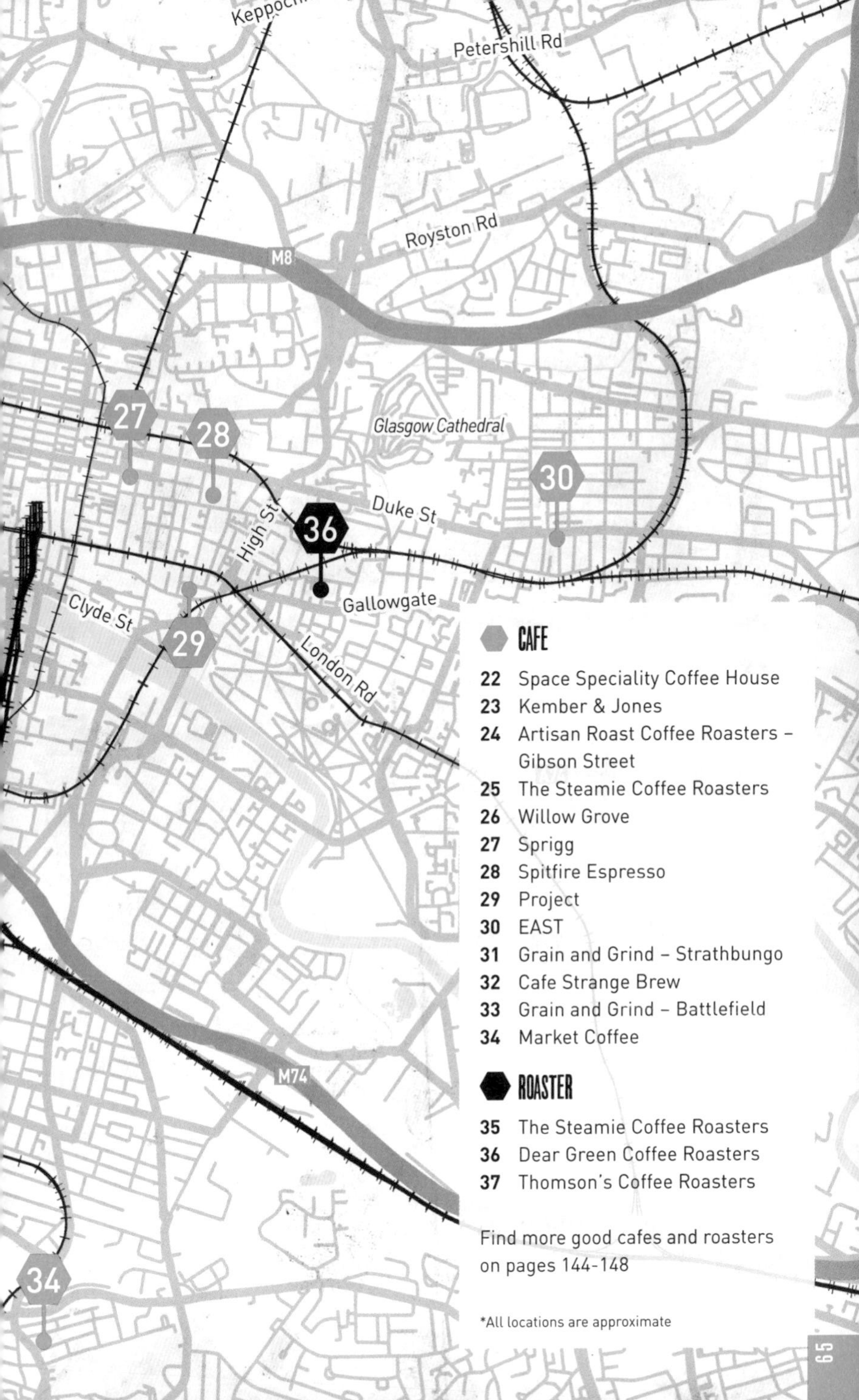
Keppoch
Petershill Rd
Royston Rd
M8
Glasgow Cathedral
Duke St
High St
Gallowgate
Clyde St
London Rd
M74
27
28
29
30
34
36
CAFE
22 Space Speciality Coffee House
23 Kember & Jones
24 Artisan Roast Coffee Roasters – Gibson Street
25 The Steamie Coffee Roasters
26 Willow Grove
27 Sprigg
28 Spitfire Espresso
29 Project
30 EAST
31 Grain and Grind – Strathbungo
32 Cafe Strange Brew
33 Grain and Grind – Battlefield
34 Market Coffee
ROASTER
35 The Steamie Coffee Roasters
36 Dear Green Coffee Roasters
37 Thomson's Coffee Roasters
Find more good cafes and roasters on pages 144-148
*All locations are approximate

MAP № 19 ST MOCHA COFFEE SHOP AND ICE CREAM PARLOUR

Main Street, Balmaha, Loch Lomond, Glasgow, G63 0JQ

Stumbling upon a coffee shop serving house-roasted beans is no biggie in Edinburgh or Glasgow but discovering a cafe-roastery hybrid in Loch Lomond which makes its own ice cream is something of a scoop.

With its Giesen roaster at the back of the shop supplying the Mazzer grinder with a perfectly bronzed stock of espresso-ready beans, this kooky gem is serving Balmaha's speciality-savvy visitors something special. Ask nicely and you may even get a peek at the roasting in action.

INSIDER'S TIP 50P FROM EVERY BAG OF LOCH LOMOND COFFEE SOLD GOES TO RED SQUIRREL CONSERVATION INITIATIVES

The Loch Lomond beans share airtime with guest roasts from Scottish favourites Dear Green, Unorthodox and Tin Donkey, while a selection of seriously good St Mocha-made ice creams also tussle for the limelight.

After successfully launching a second (seasonal) spot on Luss Pier in 2016, the St Mocha family is set to expand further in spring 2019 when its third venue will introduce speciality coffee and luscious ices to Aberfoyle. Lucky them.

ESTABLISHED
2014

KEY ROASTER
Loch Lomond Coffee Co.

BREWING METHOD
Espresso

MACHINE
La Marzocco PB

GRINDER
Mazzer Kold

OPENING HOURS
Mon-Sun **10**am-**6**pm

www.stmocha.co.uk T: 01360 870357

@stmocha @stmochacoffee @stmochacoffee

MAP № 20 THE BUFFET BOX

Media House, 1a Dunnswood Road, Wardpark South, Cumbernauld, G67 3EN

In need of a restorative cure after a big night out? Got an unsociably early start? Fear not, The Buffet Box has you covered – care of its mega 10-item Scottish breakfast featuring all the faves from a local award-winning butcher.

Alongside greedy portions of crispy bacon, sausages and black pudding, you can also pick up your 6am jolt: choose between the chocolatey caramel goodness of Unorthodox Roasters' Wee Stoater or start the day the traditional way with Thomson's St Vincent Roast.

Alan Kirkwood and his friendly gang encourage you to feel at home, spread the papers, fire up the laptop and indulge.

CAFFEINE OVERLOAD? TRY A BEETROOT, TURMERIC OR MATCHA BREW

All the specials are seasonal and range from a 21-day-matured rump steak sandwich to freshly cut salads and a wickedly decadent giant gypsy cream biscuit.

Plus, there's always a single origin guest – usually South American – to perk up your palate, courtesy of the likes of Glasgow's Dear Green.

ESTABLISHED
2010

KEY ROASTER
Multiple roasters

BREWING METHOD
Espresso, Chemex, V60, french press

MACHINE
Conti CC100

GRINDER
Mazzer Super Jolly x 2, Fiorenzato, Knock Feldgrind x 2

OPENING HOURS
Mon-Fri 5.30am-2pm
Sat 6am-12pm

www.thebuffetbox.com T: 07866 784494

@buffet.box @buffetbox @thebuffet.boxcafe

100%
SINGLE USE
PLASTIC-FREE DAIRY
AND ORGANIC
BARISTA MILK
SUPPLIER
STRAIGHT OUTTA
AYRSHIRE
MOSSGIEL
Mossgiel Farm's non-homogenised, organic milk is made by the Mossgiel Girls: an awesome team of Ayrshire cows grazing the historical pastures of Robert Burns
WWW.MOSSGIELFARM.CO.UK
01290 550307

MAP № 21 KINGS COFFEE & BOOKS

12 Queensberry Street, Dumfries, Dumfriesshire, DG1 1EX

With humble late nineties roots as a Christian bookshop, Kings added a caffeinated twist to its not-for-profit plot when it moved to Queensberry Street in the early noughties.

The coffee element of the story was an instant hit and, while you'll still find plenty of literature to browse and paperbacks to pick up, the cafe earned a spot on *The Independent*'s Top 50 Coffee Shops list.

The Kings crew are always looking for new and exciting beans and often source coffee on their travels to road test at the bar (alongside the stalwart supply from Has Bean). They even teach baristas-in-waiting the tricks of the trade at regular training courses.

INSIDER'S TIP **TAKE YOUR POOCH ALONG TO THE PARTY – KINGS IS A FAVE WITH THE FOUR-LEGGED FRATERNITY**

As well as supporting community projects (*'We're more about making a difference in people's lives than making money,'* states founder Mark Smith), the cafe is also on an eco mission. Last year clingfilm was swapped for wax wrap, a hefty discount was introduced for presenting a reuseable cup and recycling was maximised. The newly pimped menu has also received a vegan/veggie revamp.

ESTABLISHED
2003

KEY ROASTER
Has Bean Coffee

BREWING METHOD
Espresso, V60, AeroPress

MACHINE
La Marzocco Linea 2

GRINDER
Anfim

OPENING HOURS
Mon-Fri 8am-5.30pm
Sat 9am-5.30pm
Sun 12pm-4pm

www.kings-online.co.uk T: 01387 254444

@kingscoffeeandbooks @kingsdumfries @kingscoffeedumfries

MAP № 22 SPACE SPECIALITY COFFEE HOUSE

540 Dumbarton Road, Glasgow, G11 6SW

There's not bags of space at this Dumbarton Road newbie but it's certainly worth pitching up at the fuschia-flushed coffee shop for incredible coffee and endless Instagram opportunities.

Space's vibrant pink La Marzocco machine, pick 'n' mix coloured coffee cups and luscious collection of houseplants may provide the perfect backdrop for social media wins, but it's what's in the cup that really deserves airtime.

THE SELECTION OF CHINESE LOOSE-LEAF TEAS ARE SERVED IN TRADITIONAL CEREMONY SETS

Union Coffee provides the goods for the house espresso which the baristas fashion into thoroughly photogenic flat whites.

The cafe's regulars are also in the pink when it comes to choosing which guest roaster will feature next. Just swing by one of the regular public cupping sessions and vote for your fave. Previous picks have included Bailies, Colonna and Curve.

A wee bill of food is befitting of the petite space. Sit in (with your pup if you like, it's super dog-friendly) and devour a slice of toasted homemade banana bread or grab a latte and icing-slicked cinnamon roll to go.

ESTABLISHED
2018

KEY ROASTER
Union Hand-Roasted Coffee

BREWING METHOD
Espresso, V60, filter

MACHINE
La Marzocco Linea PB

GRINDER
Nuova Simonelli Mythos One, Mazzer Mini

OPENING HOURS
Tue-Fri 8am-5.30pm
Sat 9am-5pm
Sun 10am-5pm

Gluten FREE

www.spacecoffeehouse.co.uk T: 07456 672726

@spacespecialitycoffeehouse @spacecoffeehouse

MAP № 23 KEMBER & JONES

134 Byres Road, Glasgow, G12 8TD

This Byres Road bastion has been consistently busy since Phil Kember set up shop in 2004. It's not surprising as the two-tiered cafe-meets-deli-meets-bakery-meets-coffee-roastery is an absolute goldmine for greedy magpies.

Every wall is adorned with something delicious – from the racks of freshly baked loaves and retail shelves heaving with artisan finds, to the counter crowded with salads, savouries and inventive bakes.

INSIDER'S TIP GOOD LUCK TURNING DOWN A MILK CHOCOLATE AND HAZELNUT CRUFFIN

Your best bet is to visit hungry, and yielding a spacious tote. Kick off with the seasonal house espresso served as cortado and a breakfast (at any time of day) of warm banana bread with crème fraîche, banana and caramelised pecans – making sure to leave room for one of the monster scones. Then browse the curated collection of cookbooks, wines, preserves and coffee kit.

While the cafe's popularity shows no sign of abating, the friendly team like to keep things fresh and this year have introduced more vegan and gluten-free options as well as expanding the range of alternative milks.

ESTABLISHED
2004

KEY ROASTER
Kember & Jones

BREWING METHOD
Espresso, filter

MACHINE
La Marzocco
Linea Classic

GRINDER
Mahlkonig

OPENING HOURS
Mon-Wed 8am-6pm
Thu-Fri 8am-10pm
Sat-Sun 9am-6pm

www.kemberandjones.co.uk T: 01413 373851

kemberandjones @kemberandjones @kemberandjones

MAP № 24 ARTISAN ROAST COFFEE ROASTERS – GIBSON STREET

15-17 Gibson Street, Glasgow, G12 8NU

This buzzing Gibson Street coffee shop makes an alluring meeting place for students, out-of-office workers and anyone nursing a hangover – as well as serious coffee lovers mesmerised by the caffeine alchemy at the brew bar.

Gather around a door-turned-table, settle into one of the quirky chairs and enjoy the results of the Artisan bean wizardry. Or roost upstairs on the mezzanine where you can peer over the balcony and watch baristas craft V60, AeroPress and Chemex filters.

All of the beans are sourced and bronzed by the Artisan Roast team in Edinburgh (where you'll discover the three sister coffee shops) so you can be assured that every single origin is fashioned from an ultra-fresh batch delivered from HQ.

THE VEGAN CINNAMON ROLLS AND SNICKERS CAKE ARE POST-BREAKFAST MUSTS

Giving the coffee a run for its money is a seasonal menu of homemade spoils. Veggie scotch eggs, steaming bowls of chunky stew and doorstop wedges of cheesecake fuel essay writing, perfectly pair with book browsing and also soothe sore heads.

ESTABLISHED
2009

KEY ROASTER
Artisan Roast Coffee Roasters

BREWING METHOD
Espresso, V60, Chemex, AeroPress

MACHINE
La Marzocco Linea GB5

GRINDER
Mythos One, Mazzer Major

OPENING HOURS
Mon-Fri 8am-5.30pm
Sat-Sun 9am-5.30pm

www.artisanroast.co.uk

@artisanroastglasgow @artisanroast @artisan_roast_glasgow

MAP № 25 THE STEAMIE COFFEE ROASTERS

1024 Argyle Street, Glasgow, G3 8LX

The folk of Finnieston have pegged themselves as rather lucky since The Steamie set up shop on Argyle Street five years ago.

Coffee fanatics love it for the ever-evolving selection of own-roasted beans, while brunchers have made it their go-to for buttery brioche french toast and skillets of Colombian eggs and colourful veggies.

The espresso house blend, Tenement, is made up of two superior high-altitude coffees and yields notes of chocolate and red fruits. Needless to say, it appeals to *all* manner of Steamie converts.

INSIDER'S TIP CHECK OUT THE STEAMIE WEBSHOP FOR BEANS, MERCH AND MORE

The absence of a traditional brew bar means you can watch the baristas craft your coffee and quiz them on which of the down-the-road-roasted beans you should pick up to experiment with at home. You can even learn how to sling 'spros like the pros at one of the regular barista masterclasses.

If you're flagging and caffeine alone won't hit the spot, pair a filter with a slab of something gooey from the "weegie board" of treats.

ESTABLISHED
2014

KEY ROASTER
The Steamie Coffee Roasters

BREWING METHOD
Espresso, Kalita Wave, V60, Chemex, AeroPress, cold brew

MACHINE
La Marzocco Linea PB

GRINDER
Mahlkonig Guatemala, Anfim SP2, Mythos

OPENING HOURS
Mon-Fri 8am-6pm
Sat 9am-6pm
Sun 9am-5pm

www.thesteamie.co.uk T: 07821 544449

f @thesteamie @the_steamie @thesteamie

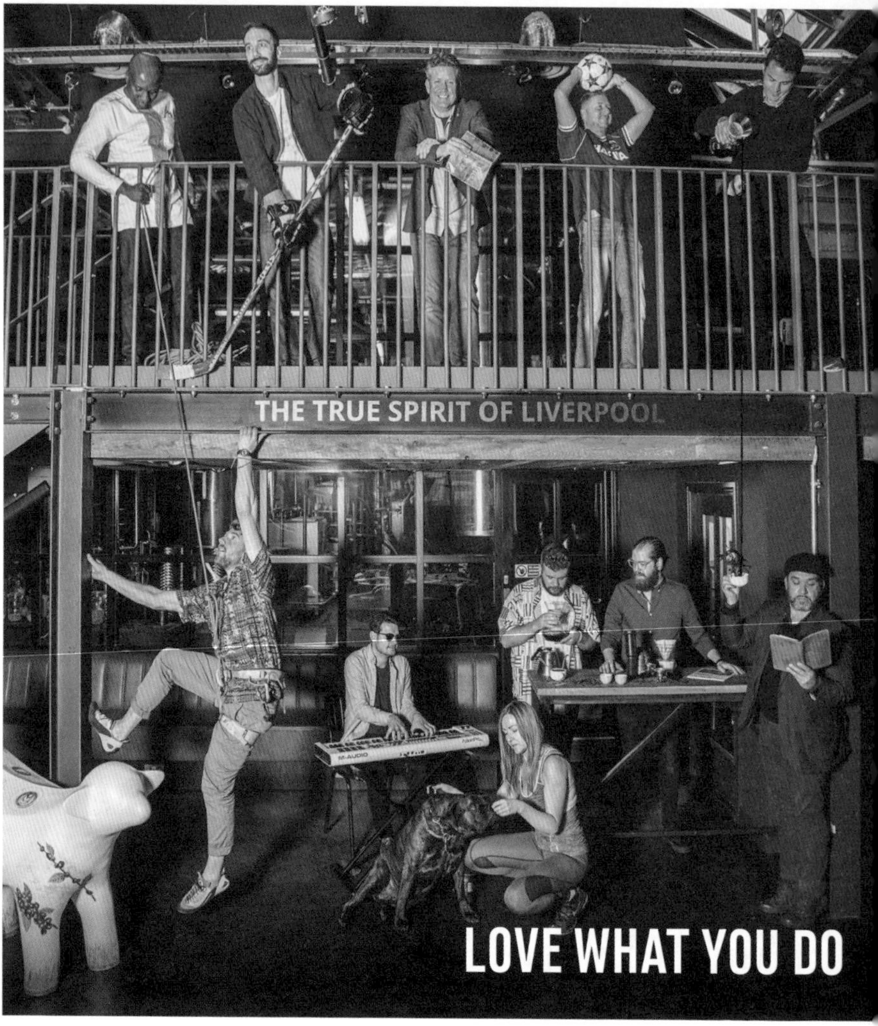

MAP № 26 WILLOW GROVE

531 Sauchiehall Street, Glasgow, G3 7PQ

Glaswegians don't need to leave the city to tour Scotland's buzzing speciality scene, thanks to this colourful coffee shop on Sauchiehall Street.

Owner Adele McPhee takes Willow Grove regulars on a palate-popping cruise of the country's hero roasteries via a rotating guest spot. Previous highlights include Kinross' Unorthodox, Dunfermline's Common Coffee and Glasgow's own Dear Green.

INSIDER'S TIP REGULARS RAVE ABOUT ADELE'S POTATO SCONES MADE TO HER GRAN'S RECIPE

While the second grinder gets about, the trusty Fiorenzato is reserved for Argyll-roasted beans. Adele used to roast with Alastair and the Home Grounds gang and developed a Willow Grove house blend with her old boss when she opened her cafe in 2017.

The bohemian hangout has been such a hit with local brunchers and intrepid coffee fans that Adele and manager Ross have taken on a fresh batch of baristas and expanded the seating space downstairs. The homemade menu has been pimped too, with more plant-based finds for vegans to sink their teeth into (tip: the big vegan brekkie is too good to share).

ESTABLISHED
2017

KEY ROASTER
Home Ground Coffee

BREWING METHOD
Espresso, Chemex, V60

MACHINE
Astoria Rapallo

GRINDER
Fiorenzato F83

OPENING HOURS
Mon-Fri 8am-6pm
Sat 9am-5pm
Sun 10am-4pm

T: 01412 373490

f @willowgrovecoffee   @willowgrovecoffee

MAP № 27 SPRIGG

241 Ingram Street, Glasgow, G1 1DA

Who said a busy city centre takeaway needs to compromise on great coffee? Hungry office and retail workers stopping at this Glasgow fave for customised food bowls revel in knowing that they'll get a decent espresso at the same time.

The first wave of grafters arrive early to assemble brekkie pots brimful with colourful ingredients (we're sold on greek yogurt, strawberry, banana and choc but the composition of each bowl is entirely down to the customer's whim). Then it's the lunch crowd's turn to agonise over which eight ingredients, garnish and dressing will make the cut.

INSIDER'S TIP JUST HAVING COFFEE? SKIP THE LUNCH QUEUE AND ORDER DIRECTLY FROM THE BARISTA

Sprigg's minimalist design makes a slick backdrop for vivacious bowls of (often veggie and vegan) goodness and a creative eating experience. Add coffee roasted by The Good Coffee Cartel, baked sweet potatoes, decadent pastries and a great selection of teas and it's easy to see why Sprigg has quickly gained a reputation as the city's go-to for customisable and fresh fast food and drink.

ESTABLISHED
2018

KEY ROASTER
The Good Coffee Cartel

BREWING METHOD
Espresso

MACHINE
Kees van der Westen Mirage

GRINDER
Mythos One, Mahlkonig K30 Air

OPENING HOURS
Mon-Fri 7.30am-3pm
Sat 11am-4pm

www.sprigg.co.uk

f @wearesprigg @wearesprigg

MAP № 28 SPITFIRE ESPRESSO

127 Candleriggs, Merchant City, Glasgow, G1 1NP

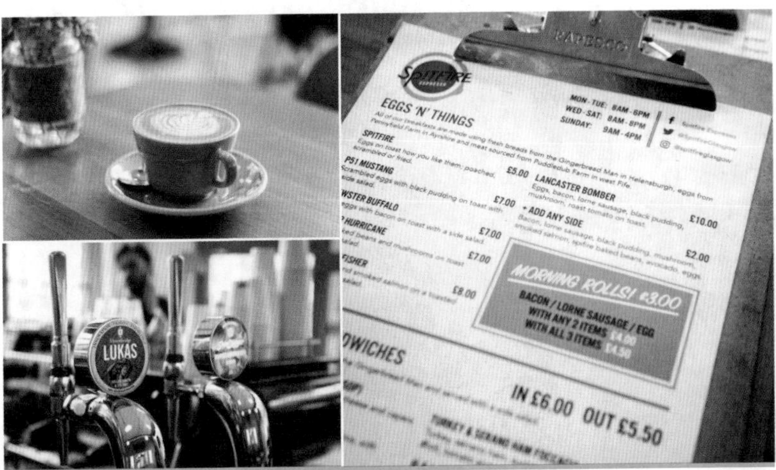

Swing by this 1950s-inspired cafe and you'll find business people, new parents and sports pros sharing table space with coffee snobs and craft beer meisters: all walks of life congregate here to get their fill of Glasgow-roasted coffee.

The city's vegans and craft brew fans let out a small squeal of excitement when Spitfire introduced a plant-based menu (in addition to its popular all-day brekkie bill) and installed two beer taps last year.

The popular venue has been a mecca for NZ-style (read: expertly caffeinated) brunching since founder Danny Gorton started slinging espresso in Merchant City in 2015, and the fresh additions – which also include more outdoor seating and a revamped lunch menu – are attracting further fans.

INSIDER'S TIP THE GLUTEN-FREE BROWNIES ARE VERY POSSIBLY THE BEST IN GLASGOW

Just visiting the city? Try not to get *too* attached to the house Gunnerbean blend as it's crafted exclusively for Spitfire at Thomson's Glasgow roastery. You can, however, pick up a bag to take home – along with guest roast beans from the likes of Dear Green and The Good Coffee Cartel.

ESTABLISHED
2015

KEY ROASTER
Thomson's Coffee Roasters

BREWING METHOD
Espresso, cold brew

MACHINE
La Marzocco FB70

GRINDER
Mythos One, Mazzer Super Jolly

OPENING HOURS
Mon-Tue 8am-6pm
Wed-Sat 8am-8pm
Sun 9am-4pm

Gluten FREE

www.spitfireespresso.com T: 07578 250105

@Spitfire Espresso @spitfireglasgow @spitfireglasgow

DEAR GREEN
CASA ESPRESSO

Number of disposables
SAVED:
SATURDAY: 9860
+
SUNDAY: 8,595
4pm TOTAL:
18,435
THANK YOU
GCF + DEAR GREEN

GLASGOW
COFFEE
FESTIVAL

HOSTED BY
Dear
GREEN
Coffee Roasters
Est. 2011

MAP № 29 PROJECT

South Block, 60 Osborne Street, Glasgow, G1 5QH

It's hard to believe that the team at Dear Green have had the time – or head space – to launch a coffee shop this year.

Yet, between roasting ethically sourced beans for cafes across the country and organising events such as the Glasgow Coffee Festival, founder Lisa Lawson and team opened Project. Funnily enough, it's in the space where the idea of launching a roastery was first sparked, seven years ago.

The light 'n' bright pop-up in artsy South Block showcases the best of Dear Green's roasts on a line-up which shifts daily. A swish La Marzocco takes care of espresso duties, while the ace team of baristas love to play about on the range of brewing gear to show off the latest single origin beans.

INSIDER'S TIP NOT SURE WHERE TO START? ASK THE BARISTAS WHAT THEY'RE DRINKING TODAY

In line with Dear Green's community ethos, the counter at Project is stocked by local indie bakers and makers. Pair a post-yoga piccolo with a plump cinnamon bun (you earned it) or cosy down among the artwork with a batch brew and a slab of something sweet.

ESTABLISHED
2019

KEY ROASTER
Dear Green Coffee Roasters

BREWING METHOD
Espresso, batch brew

MACHINE
La Marzocco Strada AV ABR

GRINDER
Victoria Arduino Mythos, Mahlkonig Tanzania

OPENING HOURS
Mon-Fri 8.30am-5pm

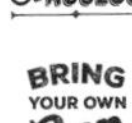

www.deargreencoffee.com

@project_bydeargreen

MAP № 30 EAST

354 Duke Street, Dennistoun, Glasgow, G31 1RB

Modern cafe minimalism and rough-around-the-edges original features combine in a beautiful creative clash at this Dennistoun find.

The local hangout thrums with atmosphere created by upbeat staff, while fragments of Victorian wallpaper peep out from coolly distressed plasterwork to create a rugged-chic backdrop.

Fairly traded beans nip over the Clyde from The Good Coffee Cartel and are carefully transformed into beautiful sips via V60 and AeroPress. Batch brews are also on tap and you can switch up your daily cup by trying out guests from other Scottish stalwarts including Artisan Roast and Thomson's.

INSIDER'S TIP **CAN'T GET ENOUGH OF THE FOOD? KEEP AN EYE OPEN FOR POP-UP RESTAURANT EVENINGS**

Cosy surroundings and stonking coffee aside, EAST's big draw is the food. Salad bowls are hearty and treats like pain au chocolat pudding demand a bold brew for balance. And resistance is futile against the gluten-free pancakes. High-stacked and chunky, they come fruitily topped (look for specials like lemon zest and rhubarb) or basking in offbeat savouriness (bacon and toasted banana, anyone?). Mercy.

ESTABLISHED
2018

KEY ROASTER
The Good Coffee Cartel

BREWING METHOD
Espresso, V60, batch brew, AeroPress

MACHINE
Wega

GRINDER
Mythos One

OPENING HOURS
Mon-Fri 7.30am-5.30pm
Sat 8.30am-5.30pm
Sun 8.30am-5pm

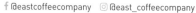

f @eastcoffeecompany @east_coffeecompany

MAP № 31 GRAIN AND GRIND - STRATHBUNGO

742 Pollokshaws Road, Glasgow, G41 2AE

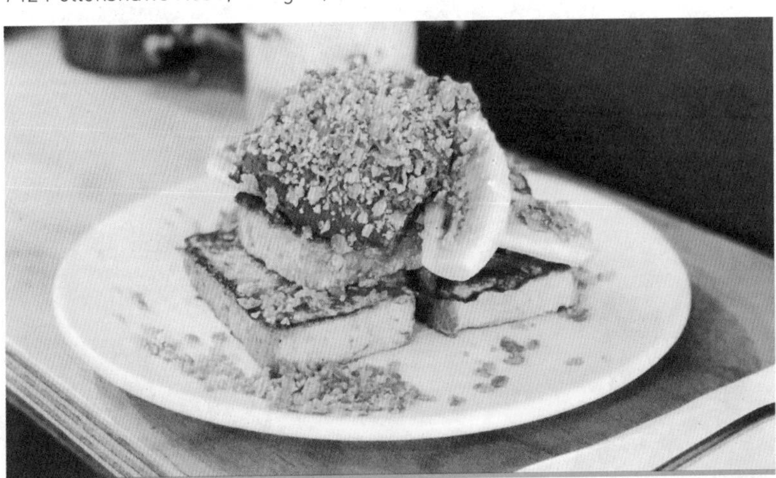

It's been a busy year at Grain and Grind. Not only did the popular indie welcome a sister shop (a 15 minute dash across Queen's Park) to the family, it also had a fresh rebrand.

The roasting operation relocated to a roomier outpost on Battlefield Road, and the Strathbungo venue now focuses on fantastic filter coffee and a curated menu of simple yet delicious dishes.

TAKE YOUR PUP ALONG – GRAIN AND GRIND IS SUPER DOG FRIENDLY

Own-roasted beans are brewed via V60, AeroPress and Chemex and served with a side of great chat and slices of gooey chocolate brownie. If you're after some serious sustenance, a seasonal menu assembles fresh and local produce between – or on top of – Freedom Bakery bread.

The peaceful spot is a freelancers' paradise with cosy nooks in which to hunker down with a fruity cold brew and chocolate and hazelnut stuffed doughnut. It's equally popular with laid-back brunchers who want to ease into the weekend with silky flat whites and baked eggs.

ESTABLISHED
2017

KEY ROASTER
Grain and Grind

BREWING METHOD
Espresso, AeroPress, V60, filter, Chemex, cold brew

MACHINE
La Marzocco

GRINDER
Mazzer Robur

OPENING HOURS
Mon-Fri 7.30am-6pm
Sat-Sun 9am-6pm

www.grainandgrind.co.uk T: 01413 286557

@grainandgrind @grainandgrind @grainandgrindgla

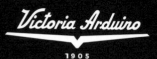

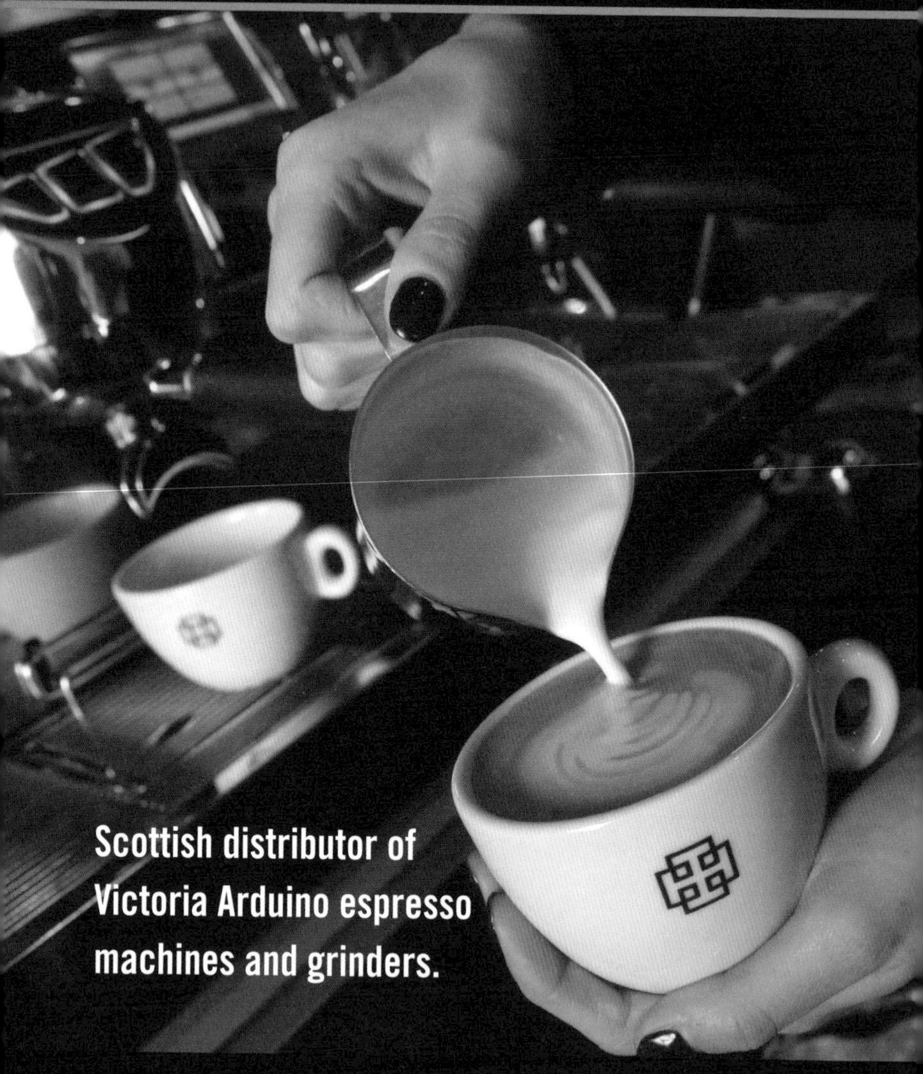

MAP № 32 CAFE STRANGE BREW

1082 Pollokshaws Road, Glasgow, G41 3XA

The creative bunch at this Glasgow fave are redefining cafe food – a regular avo on toast affair it certainly isn't.

Founding chef Laurie Macmillan likes to riff on the classics and, come the weekend, serial brunchers happily queue for her ox cheek ragu baked eggs, mulled pear pancakes and ham hock mac 'n' cheese.

INSIDER'S TIP STRANGE BREW CELEB REGULARS INCLUDE KEVIN BRIDGES AND BOBBY GILLESPIE

It's no surprise then that the laid-back gaff (no reservations, sorry) has been raking in the awards since it burst onto the scene in 2015. Gongs include two Best Cafe In Glasgow titles, *The List* People's Choice Award and a mention in the city's 2019 *Lonely Planet Guide*.

Stumping up the ingredients for the incredible grub is a legion of Scottish producers. Same goes for the cracking espresso-based coffee offering which is supplied by local roastery Dear Green. In summer, Edinburgh's Brew Lab provides the goods for a lip-puckeringly refreshing cold brew.

ESTABLISHED
2015

KEY ROASTER
Dear Green Coffee Roasters

BREWING METHOD
Espresso

MACHINE
Conti

GRINDER
Eureka Zenith 65E

OPENING HOURS
Mon-Sun 9am-5pm

T: 01414 407290

@cafestrangebrew @cafestrangebrew @cafe_strange_brew

MAP № 33 GRAIN AND GRIND - BATTLEFIELD

50 Battlefield Road, Glasgow, G42 9QF

The clue is in the name at Grain and Grind, Southside's speciality coffee roaster and grain-inspired cafe. The spacious corner spot on Battlefield Road (just over the path from Queen's Park) isn't hard to miss thanks to its statement blue colour scheme and bold typography.

Inside, the clean and modern design continues with geometric wall patterns, parquet flooring and contemporary banquette seating.

However, it's not just Instagrammable interiors that tempt the rabble of coffee snobs, lunchers and students who crowd here. With as much passion going into the heady food menu as the roasted-in-house coffee, brunch at Grain and Grind is a series of sweet highs.

INSIDER'S TIP PICK UP BREWS AND LOCALLY BAKED BREAD AT THE TAKEAWAY SHOP NEXT DOOR

Settle down for the long haul with a bottomless house blend filter coffee before clashing forks with your brunch date over droolsome homemade dishes. Favourites such as braised brisket french toast with cheese, spring onion and sriracha, and lemon and raspberry cheesecake waffles topped with toasted almonds and cookie crumb are worth losing a friend (or a finger) for.

ESTABLISHED
2018

KEY ROASTER
Grain and Grind

BREWING METHOD
Espresso, filter, cold brew

MACHINE
La Marzocco

GRINDER
Mahlkonig K30, Nuova Simonelli Mythos One

OPENING HOURS
Mon-Sat 8am-6pm
Sun 9am-5pm

www.grainandgrind.co.uk T: 01413 874069

@grainandgrind @grainandgrind @grainandgrindgla

MAP № 34 MARKET COFFEE

1071 Cathcart Road, Glasgow, G42 9AF

Marble topped brew bar, pastel-blushed banquettes and petal embellished flat whites: Market may look like it's straight out of a glossy mag but this is a popular coffee shop smack bang in the centre of Southside.

Founders Jordan and Kate Spiers picked a spot close to home when they took the leap to launch their first cafe in 2017. *'It made sense to set up shop in our neighbourhood,'* says Jordan. *'We took inspiration from our home countries of New Zealand and Scotland and created something special for Glasgow's Southside.'*

Jordan turned to previous boss Luckie Beans for the goods for Market's much-Instagrammed vanilla rose lattes and batch brew drinks. Filter options explore the rest of Scotland's roaring roasting scene with appearances from indies such as Tin Donkey.

INSIDER'S TIP JORDAN'S A MUSIC BUFF SO A KILLER PLAYLIST ACCOMPANIES THE COFFEE

Beautifully presented and locally sourced bakes cater to all manner of free-from regimes and make a delicious sidekick to the carefully crafted coffee, while a slice of lemon drizzle and a vibrant cold brew form the perfect double act on a sunny day.

ESTABLISHED
2017

KEY ROASTER
Luckie Beans Coffee Roasters

BREWING METHOD
Espresso, filter, batch brew

MACHINE
Rocket Espresso Boxer

GRINDER
Mazzer Super Jolly

OPENING HOURS
Mon-Fri 8am-5pm
Sat 10am-5pm
Sun 11am-4pm

Gluten FREE

f @marketgla @marketglasgow @marketgla

GLASGOW ROASTERS

Photo: Tyler Nix

MAP No 35 THE STEAMIE COFFEE ROASTERS

Arch 8, Eastvale Place, Glasgow, G3 8QG

In times gone by, Glasgow's steamies (communal wash houses) were friendly hubs of community spirit. While the work was hard, it was undertaken with an eye on perfection – rather like you'll find at The Steamie coffee roastery today.

Founder Stephen Meek and his team push for excellence and sustainability, and this passion drives each stage of the sourcing, roasting and tasting process. Green beans are ethically procured from farms across the coffee-growing belt and there are currently eight roasts on the go, including single origins from Mexico and East Timor.

'THE GANG CHECK EVERY LOT ON THE CUPPING TABLE TO ENSURE FLAVOUR NOTES ARE SPOT ON'

These micro batches are roasted using traditional methods, wringing every drop of potential from them, before the gang check each lot on the cupping table to ensure flavour notes are spot on.

This year sees the release of fresh retail packaging, as well as the restoration of a Fleetwood caravan for events. There's also a revised line-up of SCA-accredited coffee courses and plans for a new coffee lab.

ESTABLISHED
2016

ROASTER MAKE & SIZE
Has Garanti HSGS 5kg

www.thesteamie.co.uk T: 07821 544449

@thesteamie @the_steamie @thesteamie

MAP № 36 DEAR GREEN COFFEE ROASTERS

Unit 2, 13-27 East Campbell Street, Glasgow, G1 5DT

After seven industrious years helping to build and develop the Scottish speciality scene, the team at Dear Green were chuffed to be named as Glasgow's Favourite Business in 2018.

It's well-deserved recognition of founder Lisa Lawson and team's tireless toil which includes establishing the Scottish AeroPress Championship and annual Glasgow Coffee Festival, bringing the *Indy Coffee Guide* to Scotland and supplying and supporting cafes across the country with ethically sourced, expertly roasted beans.

Even with all this frenetic activity going on, sustainability and ethical practice come top of the agenda at Dear Green. Recent trips to Brazil, Burundi and Rwanda have built on the team's strong network of partners – ask the gang and they'll probably be able to name the farmer who grew each of the seasonal lots.

'NAMED AS GLASGOW'S FAVOURITE BUSINESS IN 2018'

2019 looks to be just as virtuous (and busy). Plans for a cafe opening, more home brewing and barista masterclasses and hosting the UKBC heats are just a few events already in the diary.

ESTABLISHED
2011

ROASTER
MAKE & SIZE
Probat P25 25kg
Probat L12 12kg
1 barrel sample roaster 100g
IKAWA 80g

www.deargreencoffee.com T: 01415 527774

f @deargreencoffeeroastersglasgow @coffeeglasgow @deargreen

MAP № 37 THOMSON'S COFFEE ROASTERS

Burnfield Avenue, Thornliebank, Glasgow, G46 7TL

Established before coffee was even a commodity, Thomson's may be Scotland's oldest roastery but it's also one of the trendsetters steering the speciality scene.

'We've got 176 years of experience,' says managing director Russell Jenkins, *'but we embrace our history instead of being bound by it.'*

The latest innovations at Thomson's huge HQ beneath Glasgow Central Station include the introduction of tailored coffee courses, a slick machine showroom kitted out with state-of-the-art gear and a string of new direct trade coffees.

'WE EMBRACE OUR HISTORY INSTEAD OF BEING BOUND BY IT'

The roasting of the expansive range of blends and single origins takes place Monday to Thursday on the vintage Whitmee Flame Roaster and a tech-savvy Loring Smart Roast.

From Friday to Sunday, Thomson's opens its doors to the public, so curious coffee fans can sample the latest batch in the cafe before having a snoop around the roastery.

ESTABLISHED
1841

ROASTER
MAKE & SIZE
Loring Kestrel S35
Whitmee Flame Roaster 35kg

www.thomsonscoffee.com T: 01416 370683

f @thomsonscoffee @thomsonscoffee @thomsonscoffee

AREA 3

TAY RAILWAY BRIDGE, DUNDEE

CAFE

38 Habitat Cafe
39 The Bach
40 Pacamara Food & Drink
41 Zest Cafe
42 Unorthodox

ROASTER

43 Glen Lyon Coffee Roasters
44 Sacred Grounds Coffee Company
45 The Bean Shop
46 Common Coffee

Find more good cafes and roasters on pages 144-148

*All locations are approximate

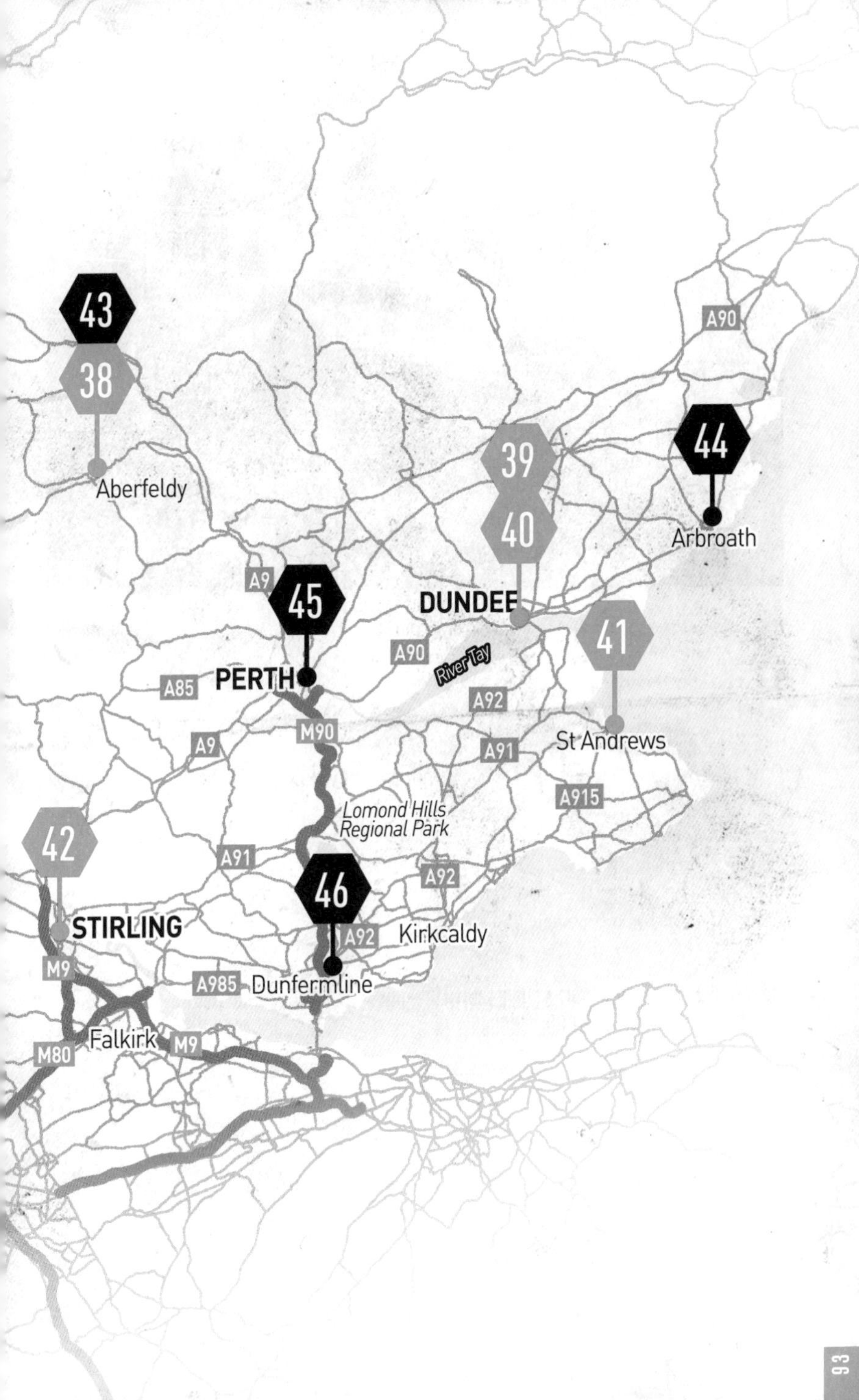
43
38
Aberfeldy
A90
44
39
40
Arbroath
A9
45
DUNDEE
41
A90
River Tay
PERTH
A85
A92
M90
A9
A91
St Andrews
A915
Lomond Hills
Regional Park
42
A91
A92
46
STIRLING
A92
Kirkcaldy
M9
A985
Dunfermline
Falkirk
M9
M80

MAP № 38 HABITAT CAFE

1 The Square, Aberfeldy, Perthshire, PH15 2DD

Since last year's guide, the team at Habitat have continued to rack up the accolades at this speciality hotspot.

Head barista Lilla Valter ended 2018 on a high when she scooped the top prize at the national AeroPress Championships, which led to her representing Scotland at the world competition in Sydney.

If you want to test Lilla's AeroPress (and Clever Dripper, Chemex, Kalita, V60 and syphon) skills for yourself, simply make the short detour from the A9 to Aberfeldy where you'll usually find her (and owner Mike Haggerton) brewing up behind the counter.

INSIDER'S TIP DON'T LEAVE WITHOUT A CUDDLE WITH HENDRIX – HABITAT'S RESIDENT GOLDENDOODLE

This cosy coffee shop on the village square is a real find for anyone crossing the Highlands. The friendly team ensure intrepid visitors leave expertly caffeinated, refuelled with quality homemade food and fully stocked with Has Bean bags from the retail selection. There's also craft beer and wine to take home if caffeine alone won't cut it.

ESTABLISHED
2012

KEY ROASTER
Has Bean Coffee

BREWING METHOD
Espresso, V60, AeroPress, Clever Dripper, Chemex, Kalita Wave, syphon, woodneck

MACHINE
Nuova Simonelli Aurelia II T3

GRINDER
Compak, Mahlkonig

OPENING HOURS
Seasonal opening hours

www.habitatcafe.co.uk T: 01887 822944

@habitatcafeaberfeldy @habitatcafeaberfeldy

MAP № 39 THE BACH

31 Albert Square, Meadowside, Dundee, DD1 1DJ

After their big move to new premises in February 2018, the cheery bunch at The Bach have settled in to their Albert Square digs and continue to deal laid-back NZ vibes to Dundee's speciality converts.

Feelgood hits at the buzzy spot start with super smooth sipping. The team champion a soft brew serve style (choose between V60, Chemex and syphon) and use Sacred Grounds beans to create flavour-popping filters. Their machine skills aren't shabby either – the espresso martini is just one delicious example.

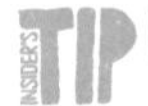

FOUR-LEGGED COFFEE FANS GET A BED AND WATER AT THE BACH

The full antipodean cafe experience is completed with a killer menu of homemade grub. Everything, from the sausage and granola to chilli jam and barbecue sauce, is meticulously whipped up in the busy kitchen. The only bought-in bits are the classic Kiwi lollies which include Pineapple Lumps, TimTams and Peanut Slabs.

Dress for all-out feasting as the weekend bill is stretchy-trouser territory. Meaty dishes such as mince on toast, harissa eggs and the Bach Bene share menu space with veggie finds such as the Bach Hash with marinated tempeh.

ESTABLISHED
2016

Sacred Grounds Coffee Company

BREWING METHOD
Espresso, V60, Chemex, syphon, Wilfa batch brew

MACHINE
Rocket Espresso RES

GRINDER
La Marzocco Vulcano on Demand

OPENING HOURS
Sun-Wed **8.30**am-**5**pm
Thu-Sat **8.30**am-**10**pm

www.the-bach.com T: 01382 869902

@thebachdundee @thebachbistro

MAP № 40 PACAMARA FOOD & DRINK

302 Perth Road, Dundee, DD2 1AU

For six years Pacamara has been one of *the* places for brunch in Dundee and, judging by the packed weekend sessions, its popularity shows no sign of slowing.

Toddler-tired mums, health-focused millennials and speciality-savvy retirees flock to the olive-hued cafe for their fill of eggs, avocado and sourdough. The kitchen squad ensure all manner of Pacamara patrons are kept happy with a menu which drops classics alongside inventive specials.

INSIDER'S TIP PACAMARA EARNED A MENTION IN THE 2019 LONELY PLANET GUIDE

House favourites such as waffles with eggs, bacon and maple butter have garnered their own fan club, while seasonal crowd pleasers include eggs and broccoli with lemon and spinach hummus, crispy kale, and coriander and jalapeño pesto.

All of this gorgeous grub is accompanied by great coffee from Has Bean, and the espresso and filter set-up also includes a regular guest roast. If you're not sticking around for lunch, pair your brew with one of the salted caramel brownies.

ESTABLISHED
2013

KEY ROASTER
Has Bean Coffee

BREWING METHOD
Espresso, filter

MACHINE
Victoria Arduino VA388 Black Eagle

GRINDER
Victoria Arduino Mythos One, Mahlkonig K30, Mahlkonig EK43

OPENING HOURS
Mon-Fri 8.30am-5pm
Sat 9.30am-5pm
Sun 9.30am-4pm

www.pacamara.co.uk T: 01382 527666

MAP № 41 ZEST CAFE

95 South Street, St Andrews, Fife, KY16 9QW

It's not just the caffeine hit which elicits a feelgood buzz at this St Andrews cafe, as every penny spent at Zest supports its social enterprise.

Set up by Lisa Cathro in 2008, the speciality cafe and juice bar helps those facing barriers to employment due to disability and mental health issues. Zest aims to help people develop new skills and find opportunities in the hospitality sector.

INSIDER'S TIP FOLLOW A BEAR-HUG-OF-A-BOWL OF SOUP WITH A SIZEABLE SLAB OF CAKESMITHS ESPRESSO BROWNIE

This work has earned the cafe a wealth of awards over the last 11 years (including an Investors in Young People 2018 gong) but the team's good deeds aren't the only reason locals (and visitors) support Zest.

It's also thanks to the cafe's hearty food and top-notch coffee. A busy trio of grinders has welcomed an impressive number of Scottish roasters this year: residencies and guest spots include Glen Lyon, Thomson's, Machina, Tin Donkey, Dear Green, Fortitude, Sacred Grounds, Artisan Roast and Unorthodox.

ESTABLISHED
2008

KEY ROASTER
Multiple roasters

BREWING METHOD
Espresso, V60, filter

MACHINE
Victoria Arduino Black Eagle

GRINDER
Mythos One, Mahlkonig K30, Bunn

OPENING HOURS
Mon-Sun 8am-6pm

www.wearezest.co.uk T: 01334 471451

f @zest.standrews @zeststandrews

MAP № 42 UNORTHODOX

12 Friars Street, Stirling, FK8 1HA

When it comes to the artisan vintage coffee house experience, few do it as well as this Stirling cafe. Amid mosaic tiles and Victorian furniture, you'll be welcomed by the waft of freshly homebaked cakes and Kinross-roasted coffee served as espresso or filter.

The Unorthodox team took over the artsy space (it was formerly Sable & Flea) at the start of 2019 and gave it their own flavour by filling the grinders with own-roasted beans.

INSIDER'S TIP DON'T LEAVE WITHOUT PICKING UP A BAG OF THE WEE STOATER BRAZILIAN BEANS

A ten-month stint in Latin America inspired Unorthodox founders Chris and Neil's passion for speciality coffee. Fast forward a couple of years and they're cooking up beans on a 6kg Giesen from their roastery in Kinross.

Ask the baristas for their pick of the single origins and take time to explore the nuanced tasting notes via V60. You can also pick up beans to drink at home.

In summer, a seat in the gorgeous courtyard is the ideal place to enjoy your brew – with a slice of banana bread or matcha brownie.

ESTABLISHED
2019

KEY ROASTER
Unorthodox Roasters

BREWING METHOD
Espresso, V60, pourover

MACHINE
La Marzocco Linea Classic

GRINDER
Mazzer Major, Mazzer Minor

OPENING HOURS
Wed-Sun 9am-5pm

www.unorthodoxroasters.co.uk T: 07856 865065

f @unorthodoxroasters @unorthodoxroasters

AREA 3 ROASTERS

Photo: Nathan Dumlao

MAP 43 GLEN LYON COFFEE ROASTERS

Aberfeldy Business Park, Dunkeld Road, Aberfeldy, Perthshire, PH15 2AQ

Glen Lyon's enthusiasm for sustainability and ethical practices doesn't stop at paying a fair price to the coffee farmers who supply the beans.

The team behind the Aberfeldy roastery also strive to cut waste and supply local wholesale customers with beans packaged in reusable tins. Chaff from the roasting process is recycled as bedding for free-range chickens and they also donate long-dated coffee to homeless centres across Scotland.

Since launching the roastery in 2011, the adventurous team regularly travel to origin on the trail of exceptional beans. Visits to Colombia and Bolivia have built strong relationships with farmers and cooperatives, and Glen Lyon now sources from 12 coffee-growing regions.

'THE ADVENTUROUS TEAM REGULARLY TRAVEL TO ORIGIN ON THE TRAIL OF EXCEPTIONAL BEANS'

Its seasonal Red Stag blend can be found on good espresso bars up and down the country, while a visit to the online shop reveals an inspiring collection of single origins to explore – including a comprehensive selection of direct-trade Bolivian beans.

ESTABLISHED
2011

ROASTER MAKE & SIZE
Probat 12kg

www.glenlyoncoffee.co.uk T: 01887 822817

@glenlyoncoffeeroasters @glenlyoncoffee @glenlyoncoffee

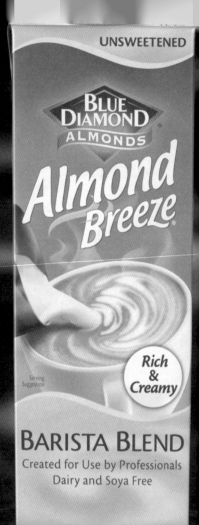

MAP 44
SACRED GROUNDS COFFEE COMPANY

Jnit 15, Arbroath Business Centre, 31 Dens Road, Arbroath, Angus, DD11 1RS

The trio behind this east coast roastery like to keep things simple, so there's no blending, grinding or caffeine snobbery here – just straight-up delicious single-origin whole beans.

Founders Kathryn, Jamie and Ian celebrated Sacred Grounds' third birthday in style at the end of 2018 (in a gin bothy with a rabble of brownie bakers, naturally) and raised a glass to a year in which the roastery's tribe of loyal followers continued to expand. The small batch set-up now includes speciality cafe customers in Edinburgh, Aberdeen and Fife, as well as a couple of award winning restaurants around Angus.

'IT'S IMPORTANT TO BE ABLE TO TELL PEOPLE WHERE THEIR COFFEE COMES FROM'

The decision to go single origin-only has paid off and their wholesale customers benefit from sharing the stories behind the beans with their own loyal locals. *'With sustainability proving to be a big issue, it's important to be able to tell people where their coffee comes from – down to the farm and grower,'* says Kathryn.

While the team sell mostly to trade, 2019 will see the expansion of the coffee subs service for home brewers.

ESTABLISHED
2015

ROASTER
MAKE & SIZE
Toper 5kg

www.sacred-grounds.coffee   T: 07808 806610

@sacredgroundscoffeecompany   @sacredgrounds14   @sacred_grounds_coffee_company

MAP No. 45 THE BEAN SHOP

67 George Street, Perth, Perthshire, PH1 5LB

It's been 15 years since husband and wife team John and Lorna Bruce first started roasting coffee in the basement of their George Street shop, yet new customers continue to discover the charms of this certified-organic roastery.

In the early days, the action took place on a trusty 5kg Probat but now the duo put their 20-year roasting prowess to use on a medley of machines (with the help of Eva and Ron) and have expanded The Bean Shop team. The roastery's direct relationships with farms in Colombia, Peru and Honduras mean each small batch has a number and roast profile for traceability and consistency.

ESTABLISHED
2003

BEANS AVAILABLE
ONLINE ONSITE

ROASTER MAKE & SIZE
Probat 5kg
Loring 15kg
Sivetz 17kg
Ikawa sample

'THE TEAM HAVE DIRECT RELATIONSHIPS WITH FARMS IN COLOMBIA, PERU AND HONDURAS'

You don't have to be in Perth to experience The Bean Shop as its online offering includes coffee, tea – many from John's birthplace of Darjeeling – gift packs and a popular postal service of roasted or green beans. But if you're lucky enough to be able to drop by to inhale the aromas, marvel at the beans behind the vintage counter or do some barista training, it's definitely worth a visit.

www.thebeanshop.co.uk T: 01738 449955

@thebeanshopuk @thebeanshopuk @thebeanshopuk

MAP № 46 COMMON COFFEE

Woodlea Stables, Inverkeithing Road, Crossgates, Fife, KY11 7ER

Choosing between the vast crop of blends, origins, varietals and processes on the market can be a mind-boggling exercise for even the most seasoned coffee drinker. So when the band of creatives at Common decided to start roasting beans from a country bakery, they opted to make the selection process as simple as possible for their customers.

This straightforward approach has resulted in four delicious roasts: Strong, Sweet, Bright and Complex. *'We stick to the fundamentals and keep it fun to make the choice easy,'* explains head roaster Katelyn Thomson.

'WE STICK TO THE FUNDAMENTALS AND KEEP IT FUN'

Explore the collection (a blend and three single origins) via the delivered-to-your-door Tasting Box – although the best way to decide what floats your boat is to beat a path to the Woodlea Stables roastery, bakery and smallholding and then drink the coffees as made by the experts.

It's also a chance to stock up on seriously good sourdough and free-range eggs from the house hens. Open to the public (8.30am-2pm) Friday to Sunday.

ESTABLISHED
2018

ROASTER MAKE & SIZE
Electric
Probat 5kg

www.commoncoffee.com T: 07921 486921

f @iicommon @iicommon

AREA
4

№55
ARTISAN ROAST COFFEE ROASTERS - STOCKBRIDGE

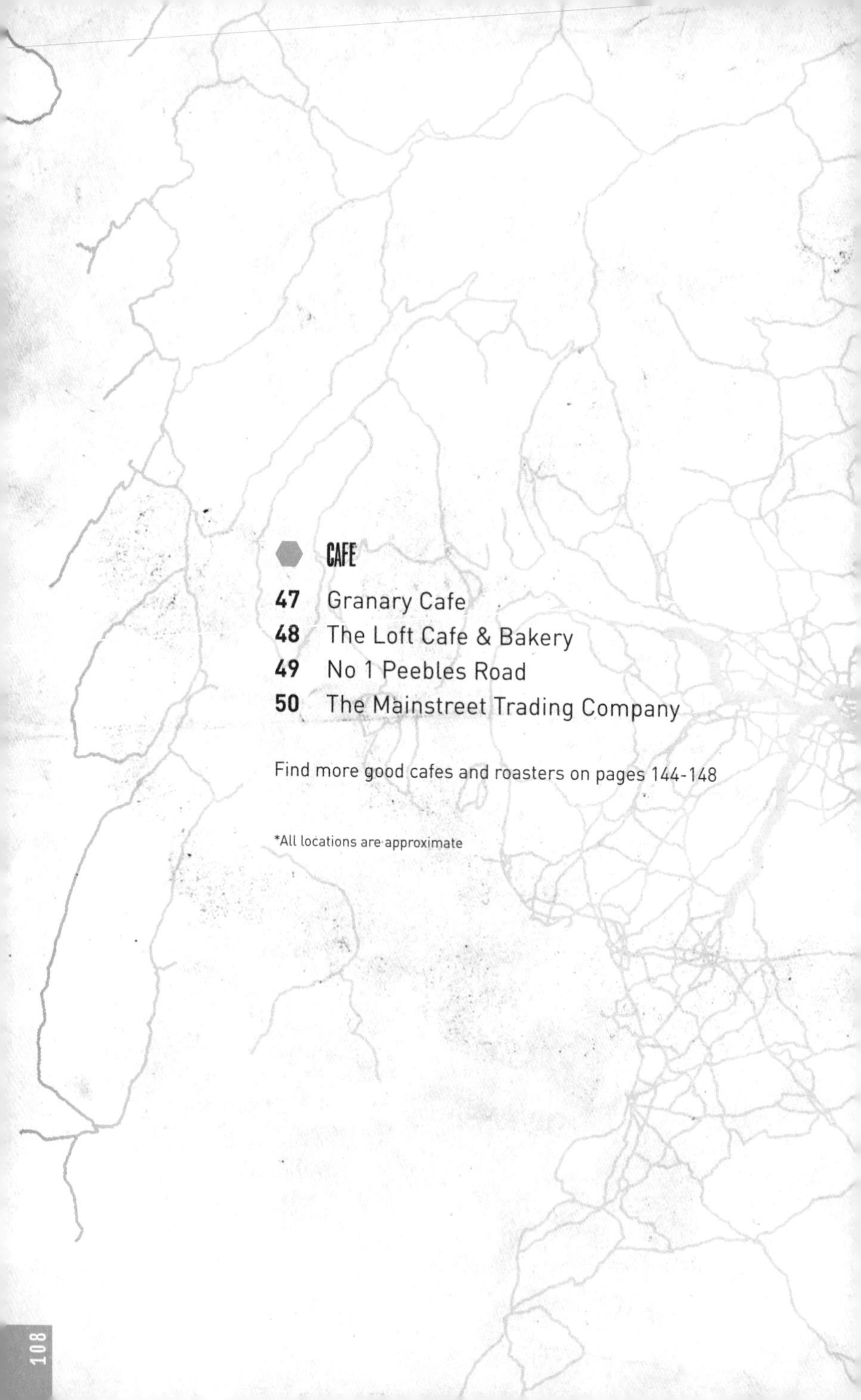

CAFE

47 Granary Cafe
48 The Loft Cafe & Bakery
49 No 1 Peebles Road
50 The Mainstreet Trading Company

Find more good cafes and roasters on pages 144-148

*All locations are approximate

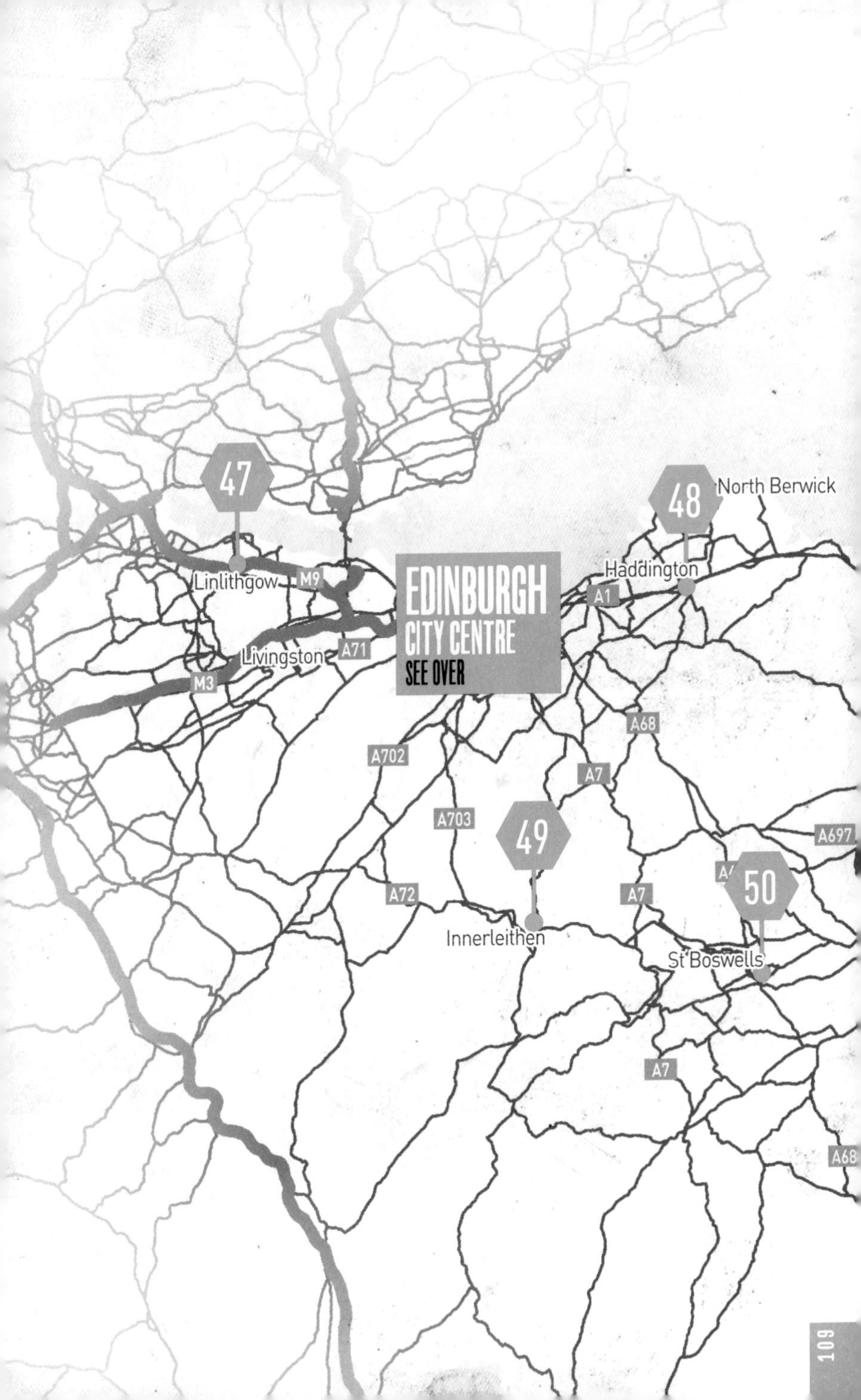
47
48
North Berwick
Linlithgow
M9
EDINBURGH
CITY CENTRE
SEE OVER
Haddington
A1
Livingston
A71
M3
A68
A702
A7
A703
49
A697
50
A72
A7
Innerleithen
St Boswells
A7
A68

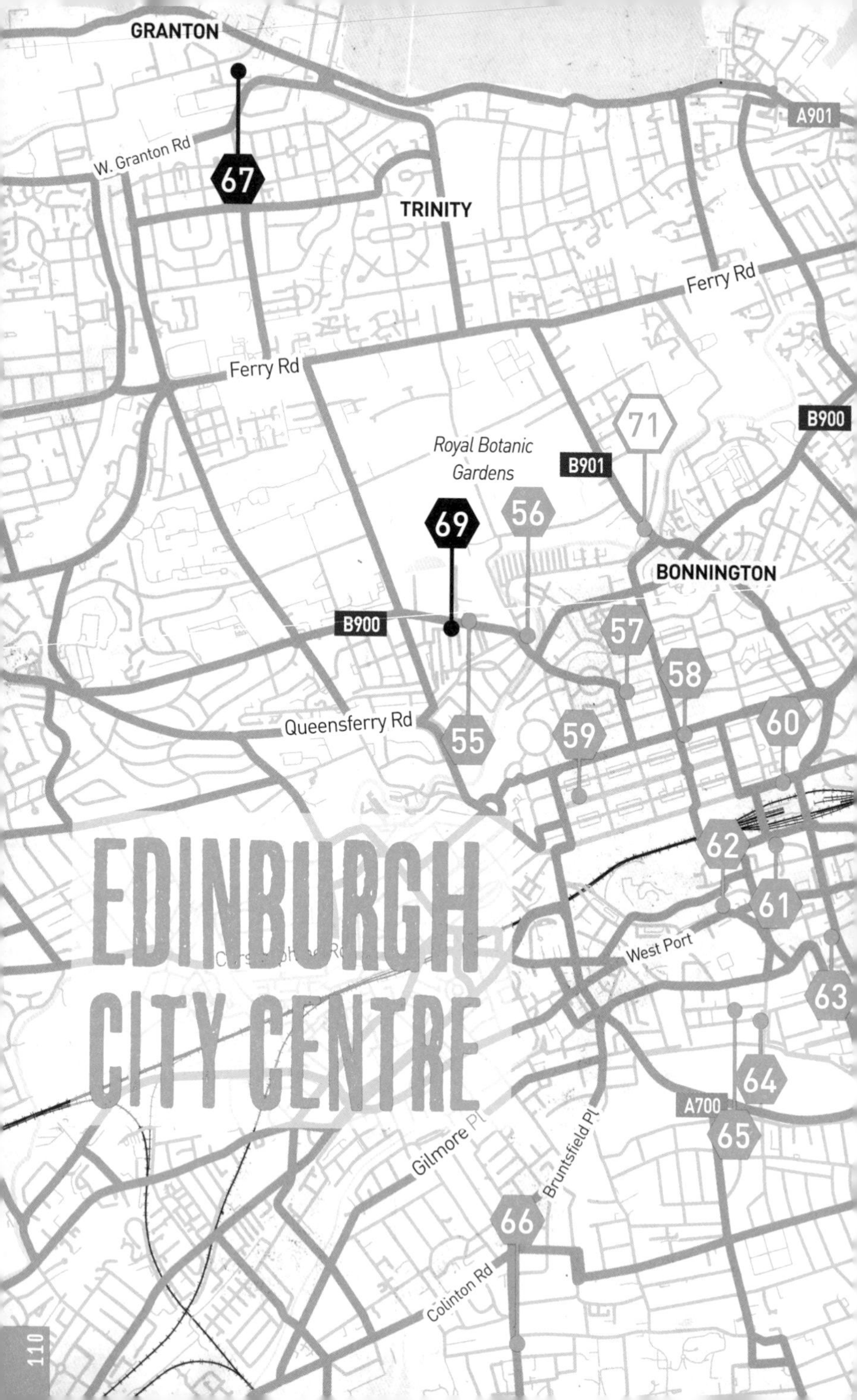
GRANTON
W. Granton Rd
67
TRINITY
A901
Ferry Rd
Ferry Rd
71
B900
Royal Botanic
Gardens
B901
69
56
BONNINGTON
B900
57
58
Queensferry Rd
55
59
60
62
61
EDINBURGH
CITY CENTRE
West Port
63
64
A700
65
Gilmore Pl
Bruntsfield Pl
66
Colinton Rd

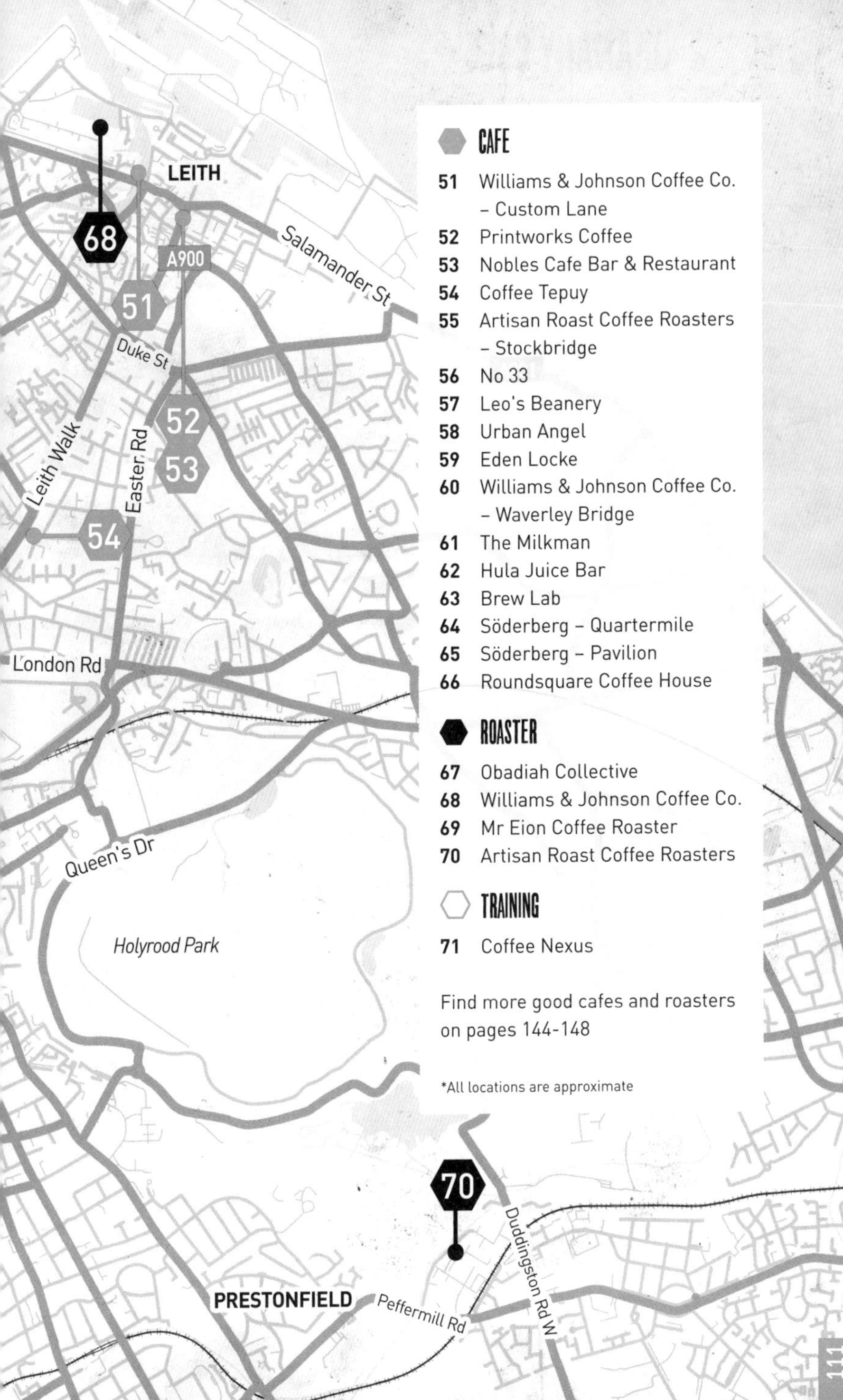
LEITH
68
A900
Salamander St
51
Duke St
52
53
Leith Walk
Easter Rd
54
London Rd
Queen's Dr
Holyrood Park
70
Duddingston Rd W
PRESTONFIELD
Peffermill Rd
CAFE
51 Williams & Johnson Coffee Co. – Custom Lane
52 Printworks Coffee
53 Nobles Cafe Bar & Restaurant
54 Coffee Tepuy
55 Artisan Roast Coffee Roasters – Stockbridge
56 No 33
57 Leo's Beanery
58 Urban Angel
59 Eden Locke
60 Williams & Johnson Coffee Co. – Waverley Bridge
61 The Milkman
62 Hula Juice Bar
63 Brew Lab
64 Söderberg – Quartermile
65 Söderberg – Pavilion
66 Roundsquare Coffee House
ROASTER
67 Obadiah Collective
68 Williams & Johnson Coffee Co.
69 Mr Eion Coffee Roaster
70 Artisan Roast Coffee Roasters
TRAINING
71 Coffee Nexus
Find more good cafes and roasters on pages 144-148
*All locations are approximate

MAP № 47 GRANARY CAFE

102 High Street, Linlithgow, West Lothian, EH49 7AQ

This little indie gem is an unassuming neighbour to Linlithgow Palace. And, thanks to its position just a stone's throw from the regal ruins (the birthplace of Mary Queen of Scots), the Granary Cafe has become as much a favourite for history buffs as coffee nerds.

Granary founder Gillian Fraser cut her teeth in the catering and events world before her passion for quality produce led her to open her own cafe in May 2017.

INSIDER'S TIP TAKE YOUR POOCH – THIS IS A DOG WALKER'S PARADISE

She enlisted Aberfeldy outfit Glen Lyon to roast the house blend, which provides a rich and chocolatey base for the espresso menu. The Edward & Irwyn hot chocolate boasts equally artisanal origins – both can be prepared with a range of milk alternatives and go down rather nicely with one of the moreish homemade scones.

On the food front, you'll find breakfast and lunch menus that are pleasingly wholesome without being preachy: think baked eggs with oozy mature cheddar and avocado, and garlic mushroom sourdough bruschetta. There are plenty of plant-based options for vegan visitors too.

ESTABLISHED
2017

KEY ROASTER
Glen Lyon Coffee Roasters

BREWING METHOD
Espresso

MACHINE
Esprezzi

GRINDER
Fiorenzato F64E

OPENING HOURS
Tue-Fri 9am-4pm
Sat 9am-5pm
Sun 9am-4pm

www.granary.scot T: 01506 253408

f @GranaryCafeLinlithgow @granarycafelinlithgow

MAP № 48 THE LOFT CAFE & BAKERY

Peffers Place, Haddington, East Lothian, EH41 3DR

Make the climb to the top floor of this 18th century stone building on Peffers Place and you'll be rewarded by discovering a sun-splashed oasis crowded with caffeine lovers and lazy lunchers.

Fuelling the cafe's buzzy chatter and brunch catch-ups is Artisan Roast's Janszoon blend. It packs knockout chocolate and caramel notes when paired with steamed milk, while those who like it black will revel in a luscious cherry bomb hit.

INSIDER'S TIP MAXED OUT? TRY THE SELECTION OF LOOSE-LEAF SPECIALITY TEAS FROM EDINBURGH'S PEKOE TEA

A consistently cracking cup of coffee isn't the only thing which gets The Loft locals' hearts racing however, and a tempting array of bakes and seasonal dishes from its busy kitchen makes popping by for just a coffee near impossible.

Arrive early to get your chops around one of the legendary sausage rolls (choose pork with caramelised onion or lentil, squash and feta) or swing by late afternoon for a slice of homemade cake.

No time for the climb? Nip into the Little Loft Shop in the courtyard for a cup to-go.

ESTABLISHED
2015

KEY ROASTER
Artisan Roast Coffee Roasters

BREWING METHOD
Espresso, batch brew

MACHINE
La Marzocco

GRINDER
Fiorenzato F84E, Fiorenzato F64, Mazzer Super Jolly

OPENING HOURS
Mon-Fri
8.30am-**4.30**pm
Sat **9**am-**4**pm

www.loftcafebakery.co.uk T: 01620 824456

@loftcafebakery @loftcafebakery @loftcafebakery

MAP № 49 NO 1 PEEBLES ROAD

1 Peebles Road, Innerleithen, Scottish Borders, EH44 6QX

Getting to know your table neighbours and partaking in a couple of polite rounds of musical chairs (and benches) is all part of the charm at this lively coffee shop in the heart of Innerleithen.

In sunny months, walkers exploring the Tweed Valley spill out onto the smatter of streetside seating with cold brew in hands. In winter, mountain bikers, fresh from the trails, steam up Peebles' windows as they defrost with Steampunk lattes and sizeable slabs of homemade bakes.

INSIDER'S TIP POP-UP SUPPER CLUBS BRING THE COMMUNITY TOGETHER ON FRIDAY NIGHTS

The year-round popularity of this small-town cafe is testament to owners Craig and Emma Anderson's passion for crafting great coffee, supporting the local community and the dash of eccentricity they add to everything (the house special is an opinion-dividing banana, bacon and marmalade toastie).

New this year is an updated brekkie offering from the busy open-plan kitchen: outdoor pursuits are well fuelled by the mighty Tattie Tower which features potato cake, mince patty, bacon and a poached egg.

ESTABLISHED
2014

KEY ROASTER
Steampunk Coffee Roasters

BREWING METHOD
Espresso, drip filter, AeroPress, cold brew

MACHINE
La Marzocco

GRINDER
SAB

OPENING HOURS
Wed-Mon 8am-5pm

www.no1peeblesroad.coffee T: 01896 830873

f @no1peeblesroad @no1_peebles_road

MAP № 50 THE MAINSTREET TRADING COMPANY

Main Street, St Boswells, Melrose, Scottish Borders, TD6 0AT

Britain's Best Small Shop 2018? You can't argue with an accolade like that. Nor would you, after venturing into Mainstreet and inhaling its intoxicating combo of coffee and books.

The cafe-bookshop-deli-homestore has put the village of St Boswells on the coffee map and stumps up a diverse offering which rotates exclusive micro lots and big-name estate beans from Newcastle's Ouseburn Coffee with guests such as Borders neighbour, Luckie Beans.

Sip espresso drinks as you peruse tables piled with books. And if you want to expand your caffeine knowledge too, join one of the seasonal tasting sessions.

INSIDER'S TIP: MAKE A BEELINE FOR THE VERY SERIOUS CHEESE AND CHARCUTERIE SECTION

On the food front, local ingredients are turned into homely dishes – often Middle East-influenced. Follow with a sweet bake as you'll never forgive yourself if you leave without scoffing a slice of Mainstreet's Guinness cake.

Pop-up evening dining events, talks by leading authors and a deli bulging with artisan produce offer further good reasons to visit. Like you needed one ...

ESTABLISHED
2008

KEY ROASTER
Ouseburn Coffee Co.

BREWING METHOD
Espresso

MACHINE
La Spaziale, Conti

GRINDER
Mazzer, Ceado

OPENING HOURS
Tue-Sat 9am-5pm
Sun 11am-4pm

Gluten FREE

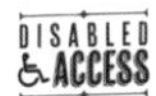

www.mainstreetbooks.co.uk T: 01835 824087

f @mainstreet.trading.company @mainstreethare @mainstreethare

MAP № 51 WILLIAMS & JOHNSON COFFEE CO. – CUSTOM LANE

Custom Lane, 67 Commercial Street, Edinburgh, EH6 6LH

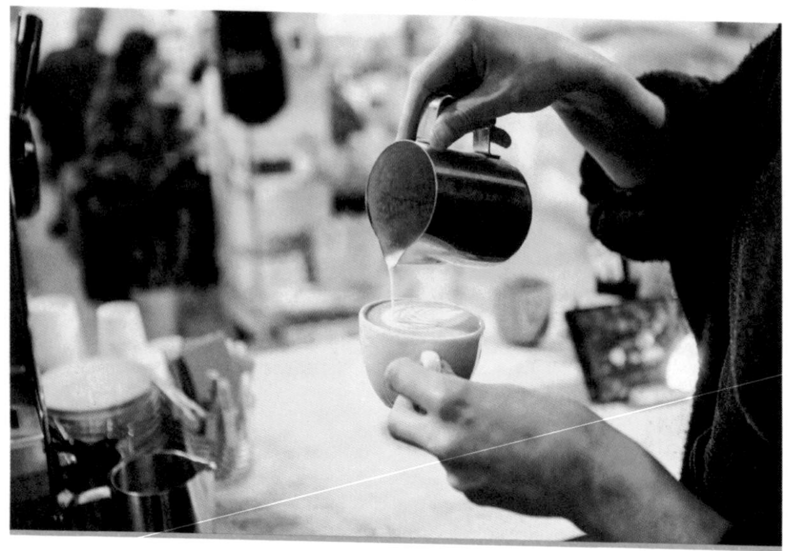

The artsy souls of Leith's waterside have had their longing for good coffee fulfilled in no half measure by Williams & Johnson.

The Custom Lane venue is a cafe and roastery in one, so beans have mere metres to travel from the Probat roaster to the Mazzer grinder.

INSIDER'S TIP EXPLORE THE EVER-CHANGING EVENTS, EXHIBITIONS AND COMMUNITY GOINGS-ON AROUND LEITH

While busy design types whizz in and out for an espresso or batch brew, those with time to linger sip pourovers and savour the scents roused from the Synesso Hydra.

House-roasted beans are meticulously sourced by Zach and Todd (Williams and Johnson) from farms across the world. The hands-on duo are also responsible for the pared-back and contemporary decor, having designed it (and even built the cabinets) themselves.

Only single origins make the cut here and from mellow caramel to fruity super-sweetness, there's a brew to please all palates.

ESTABLISHED
2017

KEY ROASTER
Williams & Johnson Coffee Co.

BREWING METHOD
Espresso, batch brew, pourover

MACHINE
Synesso Hydra

GRINDER
Mazzer

OPENING HOURS
Mon-Fri 8am-5pm
Sat 10am-5pm
Sun 10am-4pm

www.williamsandjohnson.com T: 07542 974642

f @williamsandjohnsoncoffee @cafe_williams_and_johnson

MAP № 52 PRINTWORKS COFFEE

42 Constitution Street, Leith, Edinburgh, EH6 6RS

The irresistible waft of freshly ground coffee lures passersby to the door of this little Leith cafe on Constitution Street.

Once tempted inside, curious caffeine folk will find a warm welcome and Monmouth beans pulled as espresso on the cherry red La Marzocco. Two grinders mean there's always the choice of an additional guest bean on the pourover spot, too.

INSIDER'S TIP FOR WATERSIDE BRUNCHING TRY PRINTWORKS' SISTER CAFE, TOAST LEITH

Take a seat at the communal table or nab a cosy corner and admire the local artwork as the baristas craft your brew.

Coffee is the main event here so there's no mucking about with large food menus. A small selection of homemade soups and lunch specials are scribbled on the outside blackboard each morning and provide another good reason for Leith locals to venture inside.

ESTABLISHED
2012

KEY ROASTER
Monmouth Coffee Company

BREWING METHOD
Espresso, pourover

MACHINE
La Marzocco

GRINDER
Mahlkonig, Mazzer

OPENING HOURS
Mon-Sun 8am-5pm

www.printworkscoffee.co.uk T: 01315 557070

f @printworkscoffee @pwcoffee

MAP № 53 NOBLES CAFE BAR & RESTAURANT

44a Constitution Street, Leith, Edinburgh, EH6 6RS

Leith's popular meeting place has existed in many guises since it was established in 1896, and its latest incarnation is in the form of a cafe-bar-restaurant hybrid.

Art grads Niall and Fay Taylor jumped at the opportunity to take over their beloved boozer when they discovered it was under threat of closure in 2010, and set about the task of restoring Nobles to its former glory.

Combining the original stained glass windows with new creative artwork, the pair have created a charming interior where speciality coffee flirts with the thrills of fine dining. It's no surprise that, at the weekend, Nobles is one of the city's hottest brunch spots.

THE NOBLES GANG WON THE CIS PUB EXCELLENCE AWARD 2018

Visit for the house Dear Green coffee, paired with drool-worthy dishes such as crispy pork belly benedict with sriracha hollandaise and cucumber salad, or crispy polenta with confit tomato, smoked cheddar, romesco and poached eggs. And don't forget to sample guest beans from the likes of Williams & Johnson for your post-brunch brew.

ESTABLISHED
2010

KEY ROASTER
Dear Green Coffee Roasters

BREWING METHOD
Espresso

MACHINE
La Marzocco GB5

GRINDER
Mazzer Luigi Spa

OPENING HOURS
Mon-Thu 11.30am-12am
Fri 11.30am-1am
Sat 10am-1am
Sun 10am-12am

www.noblesbarleith.co.uk T: 01316 297215
@noblesbarleith @noblescafebar @noblesleith

MAP № 54 COFFEE TEPUY

2 Crighton Place, Edinburgh, EH7 4NZ

While chatting tasting notes with the roaster over a cup of their finest coffee is becoming a more common encounter, sharing a french press with the family of farmers who cultivated the beans is still a pretty niche experience.

Spotting a gap in Edinburgh's booming speciality scene, third generation Colombian coffee farmer Yina Saurez launched Coffee Tepuy in 2018.

INSIDER'S TIP ASPIRING ROASTER? PICK UP GREEN BEANS TO EXPERIMENT WITH AT HOME

Almost every bean sold at her Leith cafe – whether ground and pulled as espresso or sold by-the-bag for home brewing – is grown on the family farm in Huila.

'We're involved in every step of the production process,' explains Yina. *'From the cultivation of the crops to drying, exporting and packaging.'*

The bronzing of the green beans is left in the expert hands of local roastery Mr Eion, which roasts the seasonal selection of strictly single origin coffees. There's a kaleidoscope of different styles brewed at the cafe so don't be shy about quizzing Yina and the team on the best way to drink the latest varietals.

ESTABLISHED
2018

KEY ROASTER
Mr Eion Coffee Roaster

BREWING METHOD
Espresso, AeroPress

MACHINE
Astoria Pratic Avant

GRINDER
Fiorenzato F64 EVO

OPENING HOURS
Mon-Fri 9am-4pm
Sat 9am-1pm

www.coffeetepuy.co.uk T: 07728 528403

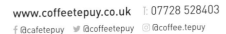

f @cafetepuy @coffeetepuy @coffee.tepuy

MAP № 55 ARTISAN ROAST COFFEE ROASTERS – STOCKBRIDGE

100a Raeburn Place, Edinburgh, EH4 1HH

Bright, quirky and deliciously cool, this Stockbridge coffee shop is the distinctly boho baby of the Artisan Roast bunch.

As you might expect, it's become the neighbourhood hub for carefully tended espresso and expertly hand-brewed filters. And, naturally, all of the caffeinated thrills are crafted from a seasonal selection of single origin beans delivered fresh from Artisan Roast HQ in the city.

The coffee isn't the only reason to rock up, however. With a recently expanded food menu which features plenty of veggie fodder, it's also become a reliable drop-in for lunch rustled up from a bounty of locally sourced ingredients.

FOR AN UNENDING SUPPLY OF BEANS, SIGN UP FOR A COFFEE SUBSCRIPTION ONLINE

Given its proximity to Inverleith Park, Artisan is also pooch friendly, and it's not unusual to encounter a vizsla alongside your V60.

On your way out, check out shelves that heave enticingly with Artisan-roasted beans – choose your current crush and recreate a quality caffeine experience at home.

ESTABLISHED
2015

KEY ROASTER
Artisan Roast Coffee Roasters

BREWING METHOD
Espresso, AeroPress, V60, Chemex

MACHINE
La Marzocco Linea PB ABR

GRINDER
Mythos One, Mazzer Grinder

OPENING HOURS
Mon-Fri 8.30am-6pm
Sat-Sun 9.30am-5pm

www.artisanroast.co.uk T: 07587 180277

f @artisanroast @artisanroast @artisanroaststockbridge

MAP № 56 NO 33

33 Deanhaugh Street, Edinburgh, EH4 1LR

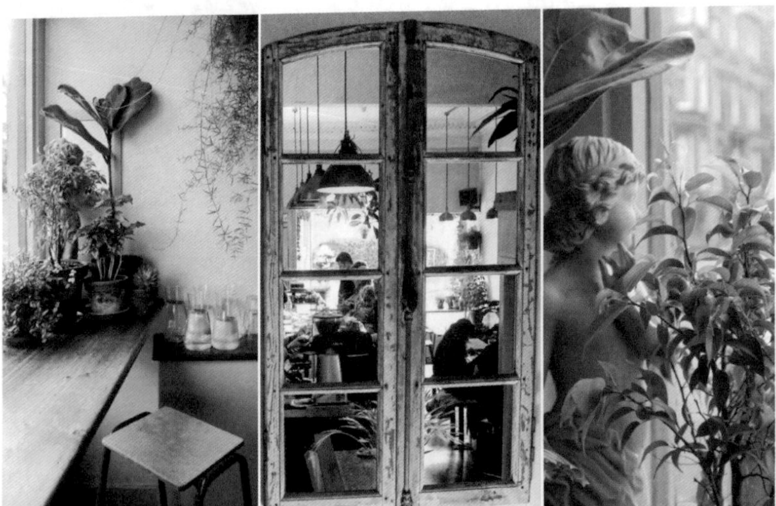

Caffeine fans who chance upon this contemporary cafe usually leave with full bellies, bags of beans to brew at home and a small grin of gratification.

The side street gem hits all the criteria for regular haunt status: a seasonally switched-up house espresso and batch brew, tasty-but-not-too-pricey homemade fodder, and a cool (but friendly) neighbourhood vibe.

Recently, No 33's small band of baristas has been having fun with a shiny new Conti X-One machine which is producing seriously impressive espresso using beans from Leith's Williams & Johnson. Currently on the go is a vibrant Ndururumo Estate AA Kenyan coffee, with support from Santa Isabel beans on batch brew.

INSIDER'S TIP VISIT NO 33'S SISTER CAFES ON BROUGHTON STREET AND HENDERSON ROW

Exposed brick walls, a crop of plants, a killer playlist and pooches snacking on treats add to the friendly feel. Stop by to sample the latest lot from the Edinburgh roasters and stick around for a bowl of homemade soup and a pastel de nata.

ESTABLISHED
2014

KEY ROASTER
Williams & Johnson Coffee Co.

BREWING METHOD
Espresso, batch brew

MACHINE
Conti X-One

GRINDER
Mazzer

OPENING HOURS
Mon-Fri **8.30**am-**5**pm
Sat **9**am-**5**pm
Sun **9.30**am-**5**pm
(seasonal opening hours)

T: 01313 328353

@cafeno33

EDINBURGH COFFEE FESTIVAL
EST 2015

5 October 2019 - Edinburgh Corn Exchange

The Edinburgh Coffee Festival features an exciting range of exhibitors and a programme of attractions including talks, demonstrations, interactive workshops, tastings and cuppings.

• Speciality Roasters • Intro to SCA Coffee Modules
• Masterclasses • Tea & Chocolate Exhibitors
• Brewing Equipment • Artisan Food

Scottish Aeropress Championships

The Scottish Aeropress Championships will again take place at the Edinburgh Coffee Festival. Further details to be announced nearer the event.

www.edinburghcoffeefestival.co.uk

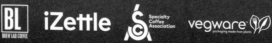

iZettle

vegware
packaging made from plants

MAP № 57 LEO'S BEANERY

23a Howe Street, Edinburgh, EH3 6TF

While Edinburgh thrives on its year-round visitors, in moments when you need to step back from the bustle, this tucked away gem is a real sanity-saver.

Veer off the pavement and down a couple of steps and you'll discover an Aladdin's cave of finely crafted caffeine, award winning cake and homely comfort. Find a cosy nook, shrug off your coat and unwind to the gentle hum of the La Marzocco machine.

INSIDER'S TIP IN SUMMER, NAB ONE OF THE STREETSIDE SEATS AND ORDER A COOLING ICED COFFEE

Stresses are soothed with help from Rounton Coffee which keeps the cafe stocked with freshly bronzed beans from its north Yorkshire roastery. Order your espresso-based drink then add a homemade black pudding, bacon and caramelised onion sausage roll plus a slab of dark chocolate and mint brownie.

This year the Beanery – run by Joe and Marie Denby since 2009 – celebrates a decade of caffeinated action on Howe Street. The family's locally sourced bill of breakfast and lunch dishes has amassed such a following in the past ten years that there are plans afoot for more Leo's events and catering projects – watch this space ...

ESTABLISHED
2009

KEY ROASTER
Rounton Coffee Roasters

BREWING METHOD
Espresso

MACHINE
La Marzocco

GRINDER
Nuova Simonelli Mythos One

OPENING HOURS
Mon-Fri 8am-5pm
Sat 9am-5pm
Sun 9.30am-5pm

Gluten FREE

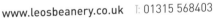

www.leosbeanery.co.uk T: 01315 568403

f @leosbeanery @leosbeanery @leosbeanery

MAP № 58 URBAN ANGEL

121 Hanover Street, Edinburgh, EH2 1DJ

Fresh from the caffeinated havens of Australia and New Zealand, Gilly Macpherson launched one of Edinburgh's first antipodean-inspired cafes in 2004 – almost a decade before flat whites and brunch became the UK coffee shop norm.

While the original ethos of serving delicious, sustainable and locally sourced food remains at the heart of Urban Angel, Gilly and the team keep things fresh with regular menu revamps.

A lunchtime line-up of smørrebrød (open sandwiches) is the latest creative refresh of the food menu.

Coffee – served as espresso, batch and cold brew – receives similar close attention and a guest slot is filled on a monthly basis by the likes of Glen Lyon, Williams & Johnson, and Alchemy. Locals who like a little consistency opt for the Urban Angel house blend from North Star.

INSIDER'S TIP PAIR ONE OF THE HAND-PICKED ALES WITH A SCANDI-INSPIRED SMØRREBRØD SANDWICH

While there's usually a queue for a table, the below-pavement hangout is deceptively roomy. If you're after a quick brew, cut the line for a stool at the bar.

ESTABLISHED
2004

KEY ROASTER
North Star Coffee Roasters

BREWING METHOD
Espresso, Bunn batch brew, cold brew

MACHINE
La Marzocco Linea PB

GRINDER
Ceado E37J, Ceado E37T

OPENING HOURS
Mon-Fri 8am-5pm
Sat-Sun 9am-5pm

www.urban-angel.co.uk T: 01312 256215
f @urbanangelcafe @urbanangel_cafe

MAP № 59 EDEN LOCKE

127 George Street, Edinburgh, EH2 4JN

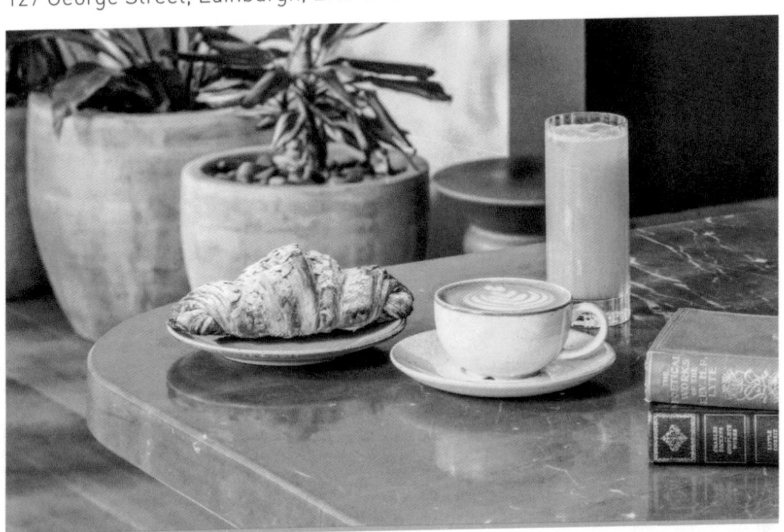

Lots of natural light and pared-back decor peppered with statement pieces make this smart speciality stop a perfect fit for glamorous George Street.

One of Edinburgh's much-Instagrammed spaces, the Grzywinski+Pons designed interior is an extension of the Eden Locke hotel above.

Its laid-back – yet ultra-luxe – living room vibe makes this the kind of place where you could easily lose a couple of hours with your laptop. Wicker chairs, knitted pouffes and a pastel palette all contribute to the zen atmosphere.

INSIDER'S TIP GET A LUXE LIFT WITH A MATCHA LATTE FROM LALANI & CO

By day, the team of skilled baristas fashion velvety-smooth flat whites using expertly roasted Common Coffee, then, as evening falls, tampers are swapped for cork screws. The short 'n' sweet line-up includes craft beers, premium spirits and a curation of wines from around the world.

You're in the wrong place if you're after all-day eats, although lip-lickingly good doughnuts and lacquered pastries are available from the marble-top bar until late.

ESTABLISHED
2018

KEY ROASTER
Common Coffee

BREWING METHOD
Espresso, V60, Chemex

MACHINE
Sanremo Opera

GRINDER
Mahlkonig Peak, Mahlkonig EK43

OPENING HOURS
Mon-Sun **7.30**am-**7**pm

Gluten FREE

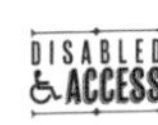

www.lockeliving.com T: 01315 264190

@lockehotels @lockehotels @lockehotels

MAP № 60 WILLIAMS & JOHNSON COFFEE CO. – WAVERLEY BRIDGE

3 Waverley Bridge, Edinburgh, EH1 1BQ

Train station coffee isn't usually worth wasting your precious caffeine quota on, but commuters rushing through Edinburgh Waverley have a new reason to risk missing their train.

Leith roasters Williams & Johnson are changing the face of station brews by taking their top-notch single origins – and fiercely indie attitude – to the station's shopping centre. The new Waverley outpost joins a sister cafe on Custom Lane.

INSIDER'S TIP CRAM YOUR CASE FULL OF THE EXPERTLY ROASTED BEANS ON SALE IN THE CAFE

Speciality beans are seasonally selected and roasted in small batches according to meticulous profiles before being whizzed all of three miles from the Leith roastery to the city centre. Aromas from the Mythos One and Mahlkonig EK43 waft out onto Princes Street and tempt shoppers, commuters and tourists to poke their heads into the bright venue.

Sip a syrupy Guatemalan batch brew or espresso alongside a buttery pastry baked nearby at Twelve Triangles. More serious hunger pangs can be quelled by soothing soups and cheesy toasties revved up with a dash of hot sauce.

ESTABLISHED
2018

KEY ROASTER
Williams & Johnson Coffee Co.

BREWING METHOD
Espresso, batch brew

MACHINE
La Marzocco Linea

GRINDER
Mahlkonig EK43, Mythos One

OPENING HOURS
Mon-Fri 7.30am-6pm
Sat 8.30am-5pm
Sun 10am-5pm

www.williamsandjohnson.com T: 07542 974642

f @williamsandjohnsoncoffee @cafe_williams_and_johnson

MAP № 61 THE MILKMAN

7 Cockburn Street, Edinburgh, EH1 1BP

This bespoke little beauty in the heart of Edinburgh is a sanctuary for indecisive speciality drinkers.

While the house espresso from Obadiah has gained resident status, The Milkman's rotation of filters tours Europe's best roasteries: recent visits include Sussex (Craft House), Berlin (Five Elephant) and Aberfeldy (Glen Lyon). Alt options are also aplenty and have expanded to include tumeric and chai latte, as well as white hot choc.

INSIDER'S TIP GRAB A STOOL IN THE WINDOW, ORDER A BATCH BREW AND WATCH TOURISTS TACKLE COCKBURN STREET

While the speciality experience is progressive, The Milkman is rooted in heritage. The central coffee bar is named after owner Mark's great grandfather, George Donald, and his silhouette is proudly displayed in the logo. The Cockburn Street space is also steeped in history – the bar fashioned from hundred-year-old wood and its sign World Heritage protected.

Located just steps from Waverley Station, The Milkman is a great first stop on any caffeinated tour of the capital. Kick off with a flat white and a flaky pastry fresh from the local bakery and imbibe a little history with your 21st century brew.

ESTABLISHED
2015

KEY ROASTER
Obadiah Collective

BREWING METHOD
Espresso, batch brew

MACHINE
La Marzocco Linea Classic

GRINDER
Mahlkonig EK43, Mahlkonig Peak

OPENING HOURS
Mon-Fri 8am-6pm
Sat-Sun 9am-6pm

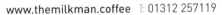

www.themilkman.coffee T: 01312 257119

@themilkmancoffee @TheMilkmanEdin @themilkmancoffee

№57
LEO'S BEANERY

MAP № 62 HULA JUICE BAR

103-105 West Row, Edinburgh, EH1 2JP

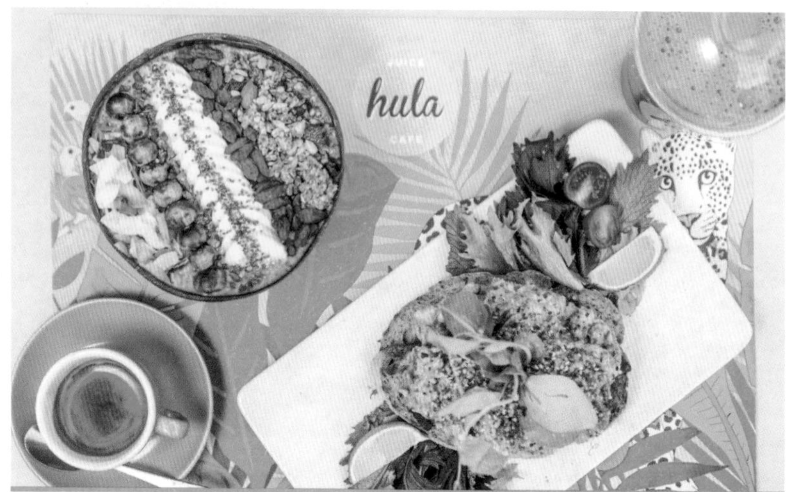

Your body will only thank you after a visit to this vibrant and buzzy tropical oasis, loved for its scrumptiously healthy food, zinging juices and consistently great coffee.

Nutrient-packed smoothies, poke bowls of luscious ingredients, and wholesome toast options are not only nourishing, they also make very attractive accomplices to Edinburgh-roasted Artisan espresso.

The friendly Hula team pay tribute to sunshiney days via bright bowls of superfoods (try the Amazon acai adorned with banana, strawberry, blueberry and coconut milk, sprinkled with chia seeds and cacao nibs) and plenty of plant-based, raw and gluten-free options.

INSIDER'S TIP CHECK OUT THE MATCHA LATTE WITH ALMOND MILK AND MAPLE SYRUP

Nestled below the castle on one of the most Instagrammed streets in the UK, the cosy cafe makes the perfect glow-cation after a morning of sightseeing and shopping. Grab lunch, restore yourself with a flat white or cinnamon latte and before long you'll be performing your inner hula dance.

ESTABLISHED
2007

KEY ROASTER
Artisan Roast Coffee Roasters

BREWING METHOD
Espresso

MACHINE
La Spaziale

GRINDER
Mazzer Major

OPENING HOURS
Mon-Sun **8**am-**6**pm

www.hulajuicebar.co.uk T: 01312 201121

@hulajuicebar @hulajuicebar @hulajuicebar

MAP № 63 BREW LAB

6-8 South College Street, Edinburgh, EH8 9AA

Brew Lab was one of the speciality trailblazers when co-founders Dave Law and Thomas Hyde started pushing quality coffee in 2012. Six years – and a helluva lot of coffee – later and the cafe's success has paved the way for its adoption into London's Union Hand-Roasted family.

Fans needn't worry about any dramatic shift in the set-up, however. Coffee is still served three ways (espresso, batch brew and pourover), Europe's best roasters keep the second grinder busy with beans of note and novices continue to beat a path to the training lab for masterclasses and barista training.

Seasonal roasts from Union have taken over the house residency on the brew bar, and the enthusiastic team ensure that the latest lot is as impressive served with milk as it is straight up as espresso.

BOOK ONTO ONE OF THE WEEKEND MASTERCLASSES AND LEARN HOW TO CRAFT COFFEE LIKE A PRO

Open late most evenings, Brew Lab's menu expands after dark to include craft beers from local brewery Pilot as well as natural wines and artisan snacks.

ESTABLISHED
2012

KEY ROASTER
Union Hand-Roasted Coffee

BREWING METHOD
Espresso, batch brew, Kalita Wave

MACHINE
Victoria Arduino Black Eagle

GRINDER
Mythos One, Mahlkonig EK43

OPENING HOURS
Mon 8am-6pm
Tue-Fri 8am-8pm
Sat-Sun 9am-8pm

www.brewlabcoffee.co.uk T: 01316 628963

@brewlabcoffee @brewlabcoffee @brewlabcoffee

MAP № 64 SÖDERBERG - QUARTERMILE

27 Simpson Loan, Quartermile, Edinburgh, EH3 9GG

By establishing its bevy of Swedish-style cafes in the capital, Söderberg has created a delicious speciality scene for Scottish fans of fika (the Scandi coffee and cake break).

The Quartermile outpost is fuelled by skilfully brewed Johan & Nyström beans and hot-from-the-oven carby delights. Pair the Stockholm roaster's Fika blend (all soft cocoa smoothness) with a sugar-encrusted kanelbulle (cinnamon bun) for an authentic Swedish coffee break.

The experience takes place in an effortlessly-chic interior (of course); huge floor-to-ceiling windows create a light-filled space, while lust-list pieces from furniture designer Norrgavel add wow factor.

INSIDER'S TIP BUY A KEEPCUP AND GET A COFFEE FOR £1 – PLUS A FREE BUN TO BOOT

The busy kitchen bakes according to the Swedish calendar, so cake fiends can look forward to trying Midsommar and Saint Lucia-inspired delights at certain times of the year.

Just visiting the city? You're in luck if you're from down south as Söderberg is also launching a Soho venue in 2019.

ESTABLISHED
2010

KEY ROASTER
Johan & Nyström

BREWING METHOD
Espresso, filter

MACHINE
La Marzocco Linea PB

GRINDER
Mahlkonig K30

OPENING HOURS
Mon-Fri 7.30am-6pm
Sat-Sun 9am-6pm

Gluten FREE

www.soderberg.uk T: 01312 281905

f @soderbergedinburgh @soderbergbakery

MAP № 65 SÖDERBERG - PAVILION

1 Lister Square, Edinburgh, EH3 9GL

Foodies in-the-know schedule a Friday lunch stop at Söderberg's flagship Lister Square site. It's not just for a caffeine pep-me-up to get them through the afternoon, but for the hot-from-the-oven sourdough pizzas.

Curve-ball toppings such as smoked salmon with crème fraîche, dill and cracked black pepper pay homage to the cafe and bakery's Swedish heritage, as does the list of Scandi-inspired cocktails (it's nearly the weekend after all).

INSIDER'S TIP NOT INTO PIZZA? TRY ONE OF THE SMØRREBRØDS (SCANDINAVIAN OPEN RYE SANDWICHES)

Beans from Johan & Nyström extend the Nordic theme to the menu of espresso-based beverages, while a selection of traditional baked goods – try the neatly knotted cinnamon buns – keeps the perfectly poured flat whites company.

Stick around long enough (the effortlessly chic interior makes it easy enough) and you'll catch one of the regular jazz evenings. If the weather's playing ball, the terrace is a great spot for evening drinks – cosy up under one of the sheepskin throws.

ESTABLISHED
2015

KEY ROASTER
Johan & Nyström

BREWING METHOD
Espresso

MACHINE
La Marzocco Linea PB

GRINDER
Mahlkonig

OPENING HOURS
Mon 8am-6pm
Tue-Fri 8am-10pm
Sat 10am-10pm
Sun 10am-8pm

BRING YOUR OWN Cup

www.soderberg.uk T: 01312 281905
@soderbergbakery

MAP № 66 ROUNDSQUARE COFFEE HOUSE

132 Morningside Road, Edinburgh, EH10 4BX

This busy coffee house on Morningside has gained a reputation for flawless latte art, and it's been such a hit that the team have introduced a series of masterclasses with the artist (barista) in residence.

Partenie McGuigan's masterpieces in milk are the stuff of legend and span from the classic "double headed swan" through to the (less conventional) "owl sitting on a branch". And, even if the one-to-one sessions don't see you hitting the barista's "Scottish crest" heights (yep, he's nailed that too), they're a fun introduction to the skill.

TAKE YOUR LAPTOP AND JOIN THE FREELANCERS AT THE WINDOW STOOLS

Providing a base for these much-papped flat whites are organic and RFA-certified beans from Roundsquare's Edinburgh roastery. The Great Taste Award winning blend is a dreamy marriage of chocolate and caramel notes and goes down a storm with oat milk in an iced latte.

Sweet thrills are provided by a line-up of local bakeries and include giant pastries, luscious loaf cakes and chunks of homemade brownie.

ESTABLISHED
2016

KEY ROASTER
Roundsquare Roastery

BREWING METHOD
Espresso

MACHINE
Sanremo

GRINDER
Multiple grinders

OPENING HOURS
Mon-Sat 8am-6pm
Sun 10am-5pm

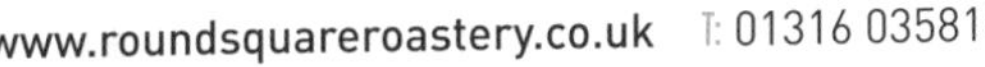

www.roundsquareroastery.co.uk T: 01316 035818

@Roundsquare_Coffee_House

EDINBURGH

Damn fine coffee...

ROA
STERS

Photo: Jon Tyson

MAP No. 67 OBADIAH COLLECTIVE

Unit 6, New Broompark, Edinburgh, EH5 1RS

Obadiah Collective is quickly gaining an enviable reputation for lip-smacking speciality coffee within Scotland's constantly evolving scene.

Mastering his craft at Five Senses Coffee in Australia, founder Sam Young launched his own roasting operation on the outskirts of Edinburgh in 2017.

Beans destined for Obadiah's 12kg Diedrich are selected based on a thorough understanding of how the conditions at origin can translate through the roasting process and into the cup.

'WE RECENTLY INTRODUCED REUSABLE TUBS FOR OUR WHOLESALE CUSTOMERS'

The team work creatively with their eclectic customer base and tailor coffee solutions to meet every coffee shop and home brewer's individual needs.

Obadiah is also pushing the boundaries of Scottish coffee culture in its sustainable sourcing and planet-friendly packaging practices: *'We recently introduced reusable tubs for our wholesale customers,'* says Sam.

ESTABLISHED
2017

ROASTER MAKE & SIZE
Diedrich 12kg

www.obadiahcollective.com T: 07481 741477

@obadiahcollective

MAP № 68 WILLIAMS & JOHNSON COFFEE CO.

1 Customs Wharf, Edinburgh, EH6 6AL

In its maritime heyday, Leith Docks welcomed exotic goods and intrepid travellers to Edinburgh, so the edge of these waters is an apt place to find a coffee company established by modern-day adventurers Zachary (Williams) and Todd (Johnson).

The pair set up shop in what's now an artsy hotspot, fuelling local workers with exceptional beans.

The guys have their noses firmly trained to the ground, sniffing out the best harvests and, as the single-origin-only selection revolves with the seasons, there's always something new on offer.

ESTABLISHED
2016

ROASTER
MAKE & SIZE
Probat Probatone
12kg

'WILLIAMS & JOHNSON WORK HARD TO TICKLE OUT THE BEANS' INDIVIDUAL CHARACTERISTICS'

Williams & Johnson work hard to tickle out the individual characteristics of these carefully chosen beans on a 12kg Probat, cooking up small batches every Monday and Tuesday in the roastery-cafe space.

A good deal of care (and a lot of experimentation) goes into making sure each batch has just the right roast profile so its natural characteristics come to the fore, ready to be savoured by discerning fans at the Williams & Johnson cafes – and beyond.

www.williamsandjohnson.com T: 07542 974642

f @williamsandjohnsoncoffee @williamsandjohnson

MAP № 69 MR EION COFFEE ROASTER

9 Dean Park Street, Stockbridge, Edinburgh, EH4 1JN

This roastery and bean store has kept Stockbridge's caffeine levels expertly elevated for five years due to its far-flung single origins and palate-piquing blends. Add to that a selection of brewing equipment and knowledgable coffee advice and it's not difficult to understand why – in addition to supplying the trade – Mr Eion has become the local go-to for those looking to create a speciality scene at home.

The team are dedicated to using sustainable and ethically sourced beans and this year founder Eion Henderson packed his tasting spoon for a trip to origin in Myanmar. The haul (a Ngu Shweli Estate and Myazedi Community lot) has already been snapped up by lovers of caramel fudge and toasted fruit-loaf flavours, though Eion promises that Myanmar coffee will be back on the bill ASAP.

ESTABLISHED
2013

ROASTER
MAKE & SIZE
Diedrich IR-5

'MR EION PACKED HIS TASTING SPOON FOR A TRIP TO ORIGIN IN MYANMAR'

Pack a reusable container (beans can be bought loose) and make your own voyage of discovery at the shop where you can chat through the latest lots with Eion and the gang. And don't forget to say hi to shop dog Mia, who's usually found snoozing on the hessian sacks.

www.mreion.com T: 01313 431354

f @mreionltd @mr_eion @mr_eion

MAP 70 ARTISAN ROAST COFFEE ROASTERS

Unit 4, Peffermill Business Parc, 25 King's Haugh Road, Edinburgh, EH16 5UY

From humble beginnings roasting out of its flagship Broughton Street store, Artisan's coffee emporium now includes an enviable collection of beautiful drum roasting machines overseen by a crack team who constantly hone their craft, passion and skill.

Working closely with Cup of Excellence head judge John Thompson, the gang source top quality seasonal greens, squeezing out every ounce of individual flavour. Employing a rigorous process of test roasts and cuppings, they strive for absolute consistency in every bag, and a Glenfiddich Spirit of Scotland Award for outstanding contribution to Scottish food culture proves this meticulous approach is paying off.

Welfare, social and environmental concerns have always been at the top of the agenda and long-term relationships are carefully forged with certified coffee growers, and farmers who achieve high ethical standards.

'THE TEAM STRIVE FOR CONSISTENCY IN EVERY BAG'

Add innovative packaging and a dedicated barista training space and it's little wonder that this roastery continues to increase in popularity, not just with cafes across Scotland but also with its international fanbase of online buyers.

ESTABLISHED
2007

ROASTER MAKE & SIZE
Diedrich 12kg
Toper 30kg
Probatino 2 100g

www.artisanroast.co.uk T: 07514 167470

@artisanroast @artisanroast @artisanroastcoffeeroasters

MAP № 71 COFFEE NEXUS

8 Howard Street, Edinburgh, EH3 5JP

This year John Thompson celebrates 23 years in the business – including a decade sharing his passion for speciality via training and consultancy.

His Edinburgh lab recently became a SCA-certified premier training campus – the first in Scotland to offer green coffee, roasting and sensory skills at this level. The fresh accreditation also allows Coffee Nexus to facilitate the passing on of the tasting spoon to aspiring pros via the introduction of Q grading courses run by qualified instructors.

ESTABLISHED
2009

'COFFEE NEXUS HAS RECENTLY BECOME A SCA-CERTIFIED PREMIER TRAINING CAMPUS'

Baristas, roasters and coffee businesses from across the UK make the trip to Edinburgh to extract knowledge from the Cup of Excellence head judge. John's extensive insight into the industry and frequent trips to origin equip him with the expertise to create solutions for speciality set-ups of all sizes.

When he's not passing on nuggets to the next generation, he's jet-setting across the coffee growing belt on the trail of new and exciting lots with the roasting team at Artisan Roast.

www.coffeenexus.co.uk T: 01315 561430

f @coffeenexus @coffeenexus @coffeenexus

COFFEE
at K.J
we LOVE coffee
So much we set up our own Roastery
We roast our own blend of green beans in small batches to our unique roast profile right here in Glasgow. Roasted beans are rested for one week before being ground on demand for our cafe
Our current offering is a blend of beans from:
·Brazil
·El Salvador
·Colombia
K.J
Bakery
Our Artisan bakery was established in 2010
We make all our bread by hand using 4 natural ingredients
FLOUR WATER SALT YEAST
No improvers or preservatives!
Our skilled bakers create our range of bread, nurturing the dough everyday. We have a selection of loaves available daily including Sourdough, rye and now gluten free.
SEEDED SOURDOUGH
BAGUETTE
SODA BREAD
HONEY & WALNUT
100% RYE

Nº23
KEMBER & JONES
PLEASE

MORE GOOD CUPS

SO MANY EXCEPTIONAL PLACES TO DRINK COFFEE ...

72 ARTISAN ROAST COFFEE ROASTERS – BROUGHTON STREET

57 Broughton Street, Edinburgh, EH1 3RJ

www.artisanroast.co.uk

73 ARTISAN ROAST COFFEE ROASTERS – BRUNTSFIELD

138 Bruntsfield Place, Edinburgh, EH10 4ER

www.artisanroast.co.uk

74 BABA BUDAN

Arch 12, 17 East Market Street, Edinburgh, EH8 8FS

www.bababudan.co.uk

75 BLACK PINE COFFEE CO.

518 Great Western Road, Glasgow, G12 8EL

www.blackpinecoffeeco.bigcartel.com

76 BLACKWOOD COFFEE

235 Morningside Road, Edinburgh, EH10 4QT

77 BOG MYRTLE SKYE

Struan, Isle of Skye, IV56 8FB

78 CAIRN

1 Drumpellier Place, Kilmacolm, Inverclyde, Renfrewshire, PA13 4HE

www.cairn-kilma.com

79 CAIRNGORM COFFEE – FREDERICK STREET

41a Frederick Street, Edinburgh, EH2 1EP

www.cairngormcoffee.com

80 CAIRNGORM COFFEE – MELVILLE PLACE

1 Melville Place, Edinburgh, EH3 7PR

www.cairngormcoffee.com

81 CASTELLO COFFEE CO. – BARCLAY TERRACE

7-8 Barclay Terrace, Edinburgh, EH10 4HP

82 CASTELLO COFFEE CO. – CASTLE STREET

7 Castle Street, Edinburgh, EH2 3AH

83 CHAPTER ONE COFFEE SHOP

107 Dalry Road, Edinburgh, EH11 2DR

www.chapterone.coffee

84 CULT ESPRESSO
104 Buccleuch Street, Edinburgh, EH8 9NQ
www.cult-espresso.com

85 DAILY GRIND COFFEE CO
18a Exchange Street, Dundee, DD1 3DL
www.hardgrind.co.uk

86 FIELDWORK
105 Fountainbridge, Edinburgh, EH3 9QG
www.fieldworkcafe.co.uk

87 FORTITUDE COFFEE
3c York Place, Edinburgh, EH1 3EB
www.fortitudecoffee.com

88 GAMMA TRANSPORT DIVISION
15-24 Comely Bank Row, Stockbridge, Edinburgh, EH4 1EA
www.gammatransportdivision.com

89 GRACE & FAVOUR
11 Roman Road, Bearsden, Glasgow, G61 2SR
www.graceandfavourcoffee.com

90 IT ALL STARTED HERE
75 Deanston Drive, Glasgow, G41 3AQ

91 KAF COFFEE
5 Hyndland Street, Glasgow, G11 5QE
www.kafcoffee.co.uk

92 KILIMANJARO COFFEE
104 Nicolson Street, Edinburgh, EH8 9EJ

93 LABORATORIO ESPRESSO
93 West Nile Street, Glasgow, G1 2SH
www.laboratorioespresso.com

94 LOVECRUMBS – STOCKBRIDGE
22 St Stephen Street, Edinburgh, EH3 5AL
www.lovecrumbs.co.uk

95 LOVECRUMBS – WEST PORT
155 West Port, Edinburgh, EH3 9DP
www.lovecrumbs.co.uk

96 LOWDOWN COFFEE
40 George Street, Edinburgh, EH2 2LE

97 MAYZE COFFEE & FOOD
974 Argyle Street, Glasgow, G3 8LU

98 MEADOW ROAD
579 Dumbarton Road, Glasgow, G11 6HY

99 NETHY HOUSE
Nethy Bridge, Cairngorms National Park, PH25 3EB
www.nethyhouse.co.uk

100 PAPERCUP COFFEE COMPANY
603 Great Western Road, Glasgow, G12 8HX
www.papercupcoffee.co.uk

101 PAPII CAFE
101 Hanover Street, Edinburgh, EH2 1DJ

102 PEKOE TEA
20 Leven Street, Edinburgh, EH3 9LJ
www.pekoetea.co.uk

103 **PRESS COFFEE**
30 Buccleuch Street, Edinburgh, EH8 9LP

104 **PROJECT COFFEE**
192-194 Bruntsfield Place, Edinburgh, EH10 4DF

105 **RALIA CAFE**
Ralia, Newtonmore, Inverness-shire, PH20 1BD
www.ralia.co.uk

106 **RIALTO COFFEE CO.**
33 High Street, Eyemouth,
Berwickshire, TD14 5EY
www.rialto-coffee.uk

107 **RIVERHILL COFFEE BAR**
24 Gordon Street, Glasgow, G1 3PU

108 **RONDE BICYCLE OUTFITTERS**
66-68 Hamilton Place, Edinburgh, EH3 5AZ

109 **SHORT LONG BLACK**
501 Victoria Road, Glasgow, G42 8RL

110 **SÖDERBERG – MORNINGSIDE**
310 Morningside Road, Edinburgh, EH10 4QQ
www.soderberg.uk

111 **SÖDERBERG – STOCKBRIDGE**
3 Deanhaugh Street, Edinburgh, EH4 1LU
www.soderberg.uk

112 **SÖDERBERG BAKERY SHOP – BROUGHTON STREET**
45 Broughton Street, Edinburgh, EH1 3JU
www.soderberg.uk

113 **STEAMPUNK COFFEE**
49a Kirk Ports, North Berwick,
East Lothian, EH39 4HL
www.steampunkcoffee.co.uk

114 **THE BEARDED BAKER**
46 Rodney Street, Edinburgh, EH7 4DX
www.thebeardedbaker.co.uk

115 **THE COUNTER – MORNINGSIDE**
The Police Box, 216a Morningside Road,
Edinburgh, EH10 4QQ

116 **THE COUNTER – TOLLCROSS**
The Police Box, High Riggs, Tollcross,
Edinburgh, EH3 9RP

117 **THE COUNTER – USHER HALL**
The Police Box, McCrae's Place,
Edinburgh, EH1 2DJ

118 **THE COUNTER ON THE CANAL**
Lower Gilmore Bank, Union Canal,
Edinburgh, EH3 9QP

119 **THE CRAFTSMAN COMPANY**
2 Guild Street, Aberdeen, AB11 6NE
www.thecraftsmancompany.com

120 THE CRAN

994 Argyle Street, Glasgow, G3 8LU

www.thecran.co.uk

121 THE GOOD COFFEE CARTEL

12 Cornwall Street, Glasgow, G41 1AQ

www.thegoodcoffeecartel.com

122 THE LITTLE GREEN VAN

North end of Bellfield Street, Portobello Promenade, Edinburgh, EH15 2DX

123 THOMAS J WALLS

35 Forrest Road, Edinburgh, EH1 2QT

124 TORO COFFEE

1484 Pollokshaws Road, Glasgow, G43 1RE

www.torocoffeeglasgow.co.uk

125 VELOCITY CAFE

1 Crown Avenue, Inverness, IV2 3NF

www.velocitylove.co.uk

126 WELLLINGTON COFFEE

33a George Street, Edinburgh, EH2 2HN

MORE GOOD ROASTERS

ADDITIONAL HOT HAULS FOR YOUR HOPPER

127 FORTITUDE COFFEE ROASTERS
Unit 6, New Broompark Business Park, Edinburgh, EH5 1RS
www.fortitudecoffeeroasters.com

128 GATEHOUSE COFFEE ROASTERS
The Gatehouse, Benn Avenue, Paisley, PA1 1JS
www.thegatehousecoffeeroasters.com

129 HOME GROUND COFFEE
Lyleston West Lodge, Cardross, Dumbarton, Argyll and Bute, G82 5HF
www.homegroundcoffee.co.uk

130 LOCH LOMOND COFFEE CO.
Main Street, Balmaha, Loch Lomond, Glasgow, G63 0JQ
www.lochlomondcoffee.co.uk

131 MACHINA
Unit 9, Peffermill Parc, 25 King's Haugh, Edinburgh, EH16 5UY
www.machina-coffee.co.uk

132 OVENBIRD COFFEE ROASTERS
Unit 3, Clifford Court, 179 Woodville Street, Glasgow, G51 2RQ
www.ovenbird.co.uk

133 PAPERCUP COFFEE ROASTERS
12 Belmont Lane, Glasgow, G12 8EN
www.papercupcoffee.co.uk

134 SKYE COFFEE ROASTERS
24 Lower Breakish, Isle of Skye, IV42 8QA

135 SPEYSIDE COFFEE ROASTING CO.
Garmouth Hotel, South Road, Garmouth, Moray, IV32 7LU
www.speysidecoffee.co.uk

136 STEAMPUNK COFFEE ROASTERS
49a Kirk Ports, North Berwick, East Lothian, EH39 4HL
www.steampunkcoffee.co.uk

137 THE GOOD COFFEE CARTEL
12 Cornwall Street, Glasgow, G41 1AQ
www.thegoodcoffeecartel.com

138 TIN DONKEY COFFEE ROASTERS
Eaglesham, Glasgow, G76 0BB
www.tindonkeycoffee.co.uk

139 UNORTHODOX ROASTERS
129 High Street, Kinross, KY13 8AQ
www.unorthodoxroasters.co.uk

Photo: Nathan Dumlao

MEET OUR COMMITTEE

The Scottish Independent Coffee Guide's committee is made up of a small band of leading coffee experts and the team at Salt Media, who work with the Scottish coffee community to produce the guide

LISA LAWSON

Dear Green Coffee Roasters' founder has been at the forefront of the Scottish speciality scene since she started roasting in Glasgow in 2011.

Hosting the Glasgow Coffee Festival, UK Roasting Championship and Scottish AeroPress Championship, the authorised SCA trainer also found time to launch new cafe, Project, at South Block at the beginning of 2019.

KATELYN THOMSON

After roasting at London's Volcano and Avenue in Glasgow, Katelyn moved to Edinburgh in 2017 to set up her own roastery, Common Coffee, with a couple of friends.

Over her seven-year career Katelyn has put her skills to the test at big coffee comps such as the UK Cup Tasters, UK Coffee in Good Spirits and UKBC.

JOHN THOMPSON

John works with coffee roasters, brands and farmers to improve sustainability, manage ongoing quality and add value to coffee.

He's a head judge for the Cup of Excellence programme and this year his Edinburgh training lab, Coffee Nexus, became the first in Scotland to be certified as a SCA premier training campus for sensory, green coffee and roasting.

DAVE LAW

Dave spent four years researching and developing the Brew Lab concept with co-owner Tom Hyde before opening the coffee bar and barista training ground in Edinburgh in 2012.

After perfecting and bringing Brew Lab's cold brew coffee to market in 2014, Dave joined Union Hand-Roasted Coffee in 2017 as head of innovation.

JAMES AITKEN

James started his coffee career in 2004 at Matthew Algie where he specialised in machine repair, installations and barista training. After ten years of machine mechanics, James took a break from servicing to join the team at Dear Green in Glasgow before launching Us V Them in 2017.

'The new project aims to provide engineering solutions for the speciality coffee community while also creating interest and a career path into coffee equipment repair with the Coffee Technicians Guild,' says James.

COFFEE NOTES

SOMEWHERE TO SAVE DETAILS OF SPECIFIC BREWS AND BEANS YOU'VE ENJOYED

COFFEE NOTES

SOMEWHERE TO SAVE DETAILS OF SPECIFIC BREWS AND BEANS YOU'VE ENJOYED

COFFEE NOTES

SOMEWHERE TO SAVE DETAILS OF SPECIFIC BREWS AND BEANS YOU'VE ENJOYED

INDEX

INDEX

T-U

V-Z

№24
ARTISAN ROAST COFFEE ROASTERS
- GIBSON STREET

SCOTTISH INDEPENDENT COFFEE GUIDE

the INSIDER'S GUIDE TO SPECIALITY COFFEE VENUES AND ROASTERS

★★★★★★★★★★

№4